McDonald.
24th Jan. 1930.

"DAILY EXPRESS"
COMMUNITY SONG BOOK

"DAILY EXPRESS" COMMUNITY SONG BOOK

Collected and Edited
by

JOHN GOSS

Pianoforte Arrangements
by
GERRARD WILLIAMS
RALPH GREAVES
S. TAYLOR HARRIS
ARCHIBALD JACOB
KATHLEEN
MARKWELL
and others

Published by
"DAILY EXPRESS"
NATIONAL COMMUNITY SINGING MOVEMENT
23, St. Bride Street, London, E.C.4

London: The London Express Newspaper, Ltd.
23, St. Bride Street, E.C.4.
Manchester: Great Ancoats Street.
Printed in England.

The BBC Men's Chorus
Conducted by Trevor Harvey
George Baker (baritone)
At the pianoforte, Ernest Lush

FOREWORD

ON the night of November 20th, 1926, ten thousand people assembled in the Albert Hall to launch the "Daily Express" Community Singing Movement.

There were a few minutes of shyness, strangeness, and timidity. Then suddenly, the spirit of song took complete command of the enormous audience. The chorus of "John Peel" swelled and volleyed round the great hall, and in that moment was born the astounding social movement that has since swept over the country like a prairie fire.

The story of the delight and the inspiration of Community Singing flashed from suburb to suburb, from town to town. Wireless had already brought the cheeriness and the friendliness of it all to millions of listeners who caught the infection and sang as they sat at their receiving sets

From north, south, east and west there poured in requests that other centres should be given the opportunity of enjoying at first-hand the wonderful thing which London had so successfully inaugurated.

It was not a question of capturing communities, they capitulated joyously and eagerly. Within a month the people of the Midlands were singing as they had never sung before. Wales, with her traditional genius for song, both found and gave inspiration in full measure. Northern cities and southern towns joined in the movement with irresistible enthusiasm.

Then came another and more dramatic development. The packed grounds of famous football clubs were turned into gigantic open-air concert centres. Twenty, thirty, forty, fifty thousand men and women provided unforgettable spectacles as they stood in wintry sunshine or biting wind to sing sea shanties, old, well-known choruses, and—most memorable of all—"God Save the King."

Villages and hamlets began to organise their own Community Singing. Churches, clubs, institutes, workshops, schools — practically every place where men and women gather—joined in.

Three months saw Great Britain turned into a land of song, and the whole country in the grip of a new force the social consequences of which, even now, are incalculable.

EDITOR'S NOTE

I WISH to express my gratitude to Mr. Geoffrey Shaw for several useful suggestions, and to Miss Kathleen Markwell for much valuable help in seeing this book through the press; and to thank the following publishers for permission to include a number of copyright songs :—

Messrs. J. Curwen & Sons for "Blow away the morning dew," "Strawberry Fair," "High Germany," "The Frog and the Mouse," "The Tailor and the Mouse," and "The Wraggle Taggle Gipsies O," from *English Folk Songs for Schools* (Cecil J. Sharp and S. Baring Gould); "Caleno Custure Me" from *Shakespeare Music* (E. W. Naylor); "Bobby Shafto" from *Songs, Ballads and Pipe Tunes of the North Countrie* (W. G. Whittaker); and "Shenandoah," "Blow the Man Down," "What shall we do with the Drunken Sailor," "Sally Brown," "Billy Boy," "Haul away Jo," "Fire Down Below," "The Sailor likes his Bottle O," "The Drummer and the Cook," "Tom's gone to Hilo," "Johnny come down to Hilo," and "Whisky Johnny" from *The Shanty Book*, Vols. 1 and 2 (Sir Richard Terry);

The Oxford University Press for "O Faith of England," "Ye Watchers and Ye Holy Ones," and "He who would Valiant Be" from *The English Hymnal*;

Messrs. Erskine Macdonald, Ltd., for "The Last Long Mile," "And when I Die," "Rolling Home," "Après la Guerre Fini," and "Way Down Yonder in the Cornfield," from *Tommy's Tunes* and *More Tommy's Tunes* (F. T. Nettleinghame);

Messrs. Boosey & Co., Ltd., for "Hullabaloo-balay" from *Six Sea Shanties* (S. Taylor Harris) and "Row, dow, dow or The Drum" from *Songs of Britain* (Martin Shaw and Frank Kidson);

Messrs. Hughes & Son, of Wrexham, for "Aberystwyth," and for "Land of my Fathers";

Messrs. Francis, Day & Hunter, Ltd., for the words of the chorus of "Pack up your troubles in your old Kit Bag";

Messrs. Methuen & Co., Ltd., for "The Golden Vanity" and "The Cottage well Thatched with Straw" from *Songs of the West* (S. Baring Gould), and "Let Bucks a-hunting go" from *A Garland of Country Song* (S. Baring Gould and H. F. Sheppard);

Messrs. J. B. Cramer & Co., Ltd., for "Twankydillo" from *English County Songs* (Lucy S. Broadwood and J. E. Fuller Maitland) and "Shule Agra" from *Songs of the Four Nations* (Sir Harold Boulton and Arthur Somervell); also for "Ould John Braddleum";

Messrs. Chappell & Co., Ltd., for the words of "Come, here's to Robin Hood";

JOHN GOSS.

Lancaster Gate, *February*, 1927.

CONTENTS

SONGS

SONGS—continued

ROUNDS AND CANONS

FOR THE VERY YOUNG

THE AGINCOURT SONG

Arr. GERRARD WILLIAMS

Our King went forth to Nor-man-dy, With grace and might of chiv-al-ry: The God for Him wrought marv'lous-ly, Where-fore Eng-land may call and cry

Then for-sooth that Knight come-ly, In Ag-in-court field he fought man-ly: Through grace of God most migh-ty, He had both the field and the vic-to-ry.

Their dukes and earls, lords and bar-ons, Were ta-ken and slain and that well soon: And some were led in-to Lon-don, With joy and mirth and great re-nown.

The gra-cious God now save our King, His peo-ple and all his well-will-ing: Give him good life and good end-ing, That we with mirth may safe-ly sing.

De - o gra - ti - as, De - o gra-ti-as An - gli - a red - de pro vic-to - ri - a.

A-HUNTING WE WILL GO

HENRY FIELDING

Arr. S. TAYLOR HARRIS

*ALL PEOPLE THAT ON EARTH DO DWELL
"OLD HUNDREDTH"

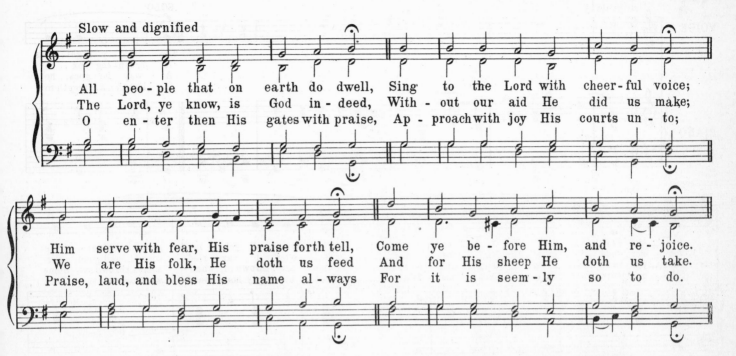

For why? the Lord our God is good:
  His mercy is for ever sure;
  His truth at all times firmly stood,
  And shall from age to age endure.

To Father, Son, and Holy Ghost,
  The God whom heaven and earth adore,
From men and from the angel-host
  Be praise and glory evermore.

* From "The English Hymnal"

*FIGHT THE GOOD FIGHT
"DUKE STREET"

J. HATTON

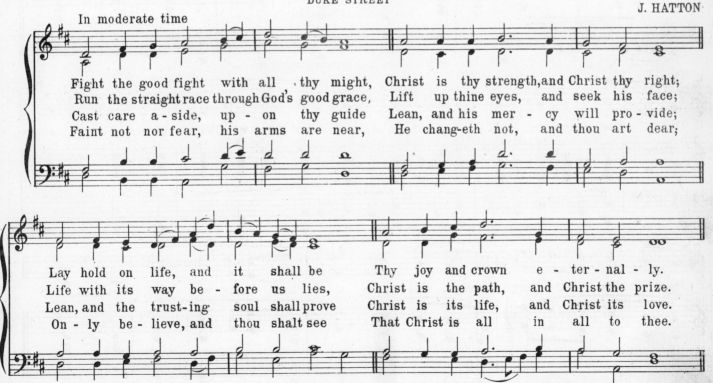

* From "The English Hymnal"

ALL THROUGH THE NIGHT

Arr. RALPH GREAVES

THE ANGLER'S SONG
(HENRY LAWES)

ISAAK WALTON

Arr. GERRARD WILLIAMS

At moderate pace, with good rhythm

SOLO

Man's life is but vain, For 'tis sub-ject to pain And sor-row, and
But we'll take no care When the weath-er proves fair, Nor will we and vex

short as a bub-ble; 'Tis a hodge podge of busi-ness, and mon-ey, and care, And
now though it rain; We will ban-ish all sor-row, and sing till to-mor-row, And

CHORUS

care, and mon-ey, and trou-ble. 'Tis a hodge podge of busi-ness, and
an-gle and an-gle a-gain. We will ban-ish all sor-row, and

mon-ey, and care, And care, and mon-ey, and trou-ble.
sing till to-mor-row, And an-gle, and an-gle a-gain.

ANNIE LAURIE

Arr. RALPH GREAVES

THE ARETHUSA
(W. SHIELD)

PRINCE HOARE

Arr. RALPH GREAVES

A-ROVING

Arr. RALPH GREAVES

THE ASH GROVE

Moderate speed and with accent

Arr. RALPH GREAVES

PIANO

1 Down yon - der green val - ley, Where stream - lets me - an - der, When
2 Still glows the bright sun - shine o'er val - ley and moun - tain, Still
Or at the bright noon - tide, in sol - i - tude wan - der, And
Still trem - bles the moon-beam on stream - let and foun - tain, But

twi - light is fad - ing, I pen - sive - ly rove.
in the dark shades of the Lone - ly Ash Grove.
war - bles the black-bird it's note from the tree;
what are the beau - ties of na - ture to me?

Repeat

Twas there, while the
With sor - row, deep

black-bird was cheer - ful - ly sing - ing, I first met my dear one, the
sor - row, my bo - som is la - den, All day I go mourn - ing in

rall. *pp a tempo*

joy of my heart! A - round us for glad - ness the blue - bells were
search of my love, Ye ech - oes! oh tell me, where is the sweet

ring - ing; Ah then lit - tle thought I how soon we should part!
maid - en? "She sleeps 'neath the green turf down by the Ash Grove."

AULD LANG SYNE

BURNS

Arr. RALPH GREAVES

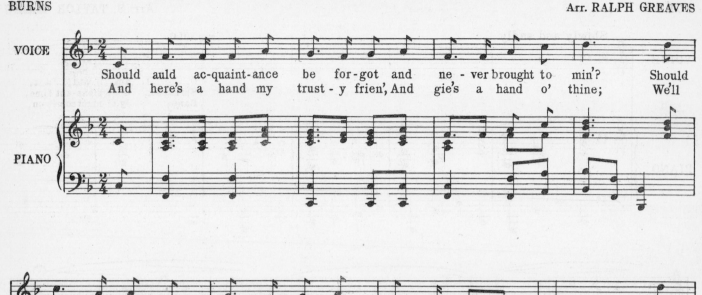

Should auld ac-quaint-ance be for-got and ne-ver brought to min'? Should
And here's a hand my trust-y frien', And gie's a hand o' thine; We'll

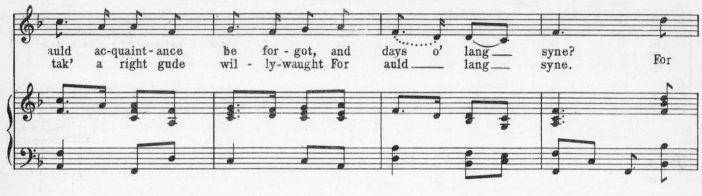

auld ac-quaint-ance be for-got, and days o' lang syne? For
tak' a right gude wil-ly-waught For auld lang syne.

auld lang syne, my dear, for auld lang syne, We'll

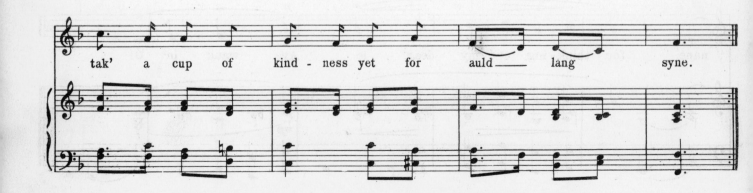

tak' a cup of kind-ness yet for auld lang syne.

AYE WAUKIN' O!

BURNS

Arr. S. TAYLOR HARRIS

THE BAILIFF'S DAUGHTER OF ISLINGTON

Arr. GERRARD WILLIAMS

5
"Give me a penny, thou 'prentice good
Relieve a maid forlorn!"
"Before I give you a penny, sweetheart
Pray tell me where you were born."

6
"Oh I was born at Islington."
"Then tell me if you know
The bailiff's daughter of that place."
"She died, sir, long ago."

7
"If she be dead, then take my horse
My saddle and bridle also,
For I will to some distant land
Where no man shall me know."

8
"O stay, O stay, thou gentle youth,
She standeth by thy side!
She's here, alive, she is not dead,
But ready to be thy bride!"

BARBARA ALLEN

Arr. GERRARD WILLIAMS

In Scar-let town, where I was born, There was a fair maid dwell-ing, Made ev-'ry youth cry_ well-a-day, Her name was Bar - b'ra Al - len.

2
All in the merry month of May,
    When green buds they were swelling,
Young Jemmy Grove on his deathbed lay
    For love of Barb'ra Allen.

3
So slowly, slowly she came up,
    And slowly she came nigh him,
And all she said when there she came:
    "Young man, I think you're dying."

4
When he was dead and laid in grave,
    Her heart was struck with sorrow;
"O mother, mother, make my bed
    For I shall die tomorrow."

5
"Farewell," she said, "ye virgins all,
    And shun the fault I fell in;"
Henceforth take warning by the fall
    Of cruel Barb'ra Allen.

THE BARLEY MOW

Arr. S. TAYLOR HARRIS

Loud and hearty

PIANO

SOLO

Here's a health to the Bar - ley Mow__ my boys, A health to the Bar - ley

Mow_____ We'll drink__ it out of a nut - brown bowl,
We'll drink__ it out of a pint__ my boys,
We'll drink__ it out of a gal - lon my boys, A
We'll drink__ it out of the riv - er my boys,
We'll drink__ it out of the o - cean my boys,

health to the Bar - ley Mow_____ The nip - per - kin pip - per - kin and the brown bowl. A

CHORUS

health to the Bar - ley Mow my boys, A health to the Bar - ley Mow_____

THE BAY OF BISCAY

(JOHN DAVY)

Arr. RALPH GREAVES

BEGONE! DULL CARE!

Arr. GERRARD WILLIAMS

BEN BACKSTAY

Arr. GERRARD WILLIAMS

Ben Back-stay was a bo'-sun, He was a jol-ly boy, And none as he so mer-ri-ly Could pipe all hands a-hoy; Could pipe all hands a-hoy, Could pipe all hands a-hoy.

Once, sail-ing with a cap-tain Who was a jol-ly dog, Our Ben and all his messmates got A dou-ble share of grog; A dou-ble share of grog, A dou-ble share of grog.

So Ben-ny he got tip-sy Quite to his heart's con-tent, And lean-ing o'er the star-board side Right ov-er-board he went; Right ov-er-board he went, Right ov-er-board he went.

A shark was on the starboard side, And sharks no man can stand, For they do gobble up ev-'ry-thing Just like the sharks on land; Just like the sharks on land, Just like the sharks on land.

They threw him out some tack-ling To give his life a hope; But as the shark bit off his head He could-n't see the rope, He could-n't see the rope, He could-n't see the rope.

At twelve o'clock his ghost appeared Up-on the quar-ter deck; "Ho, pipe all hands a-hoy!" he cried, "From me a warn-ing take; From me a warn-ing take, From me a warn-ing take."

Through drink-ing grog I lost my life The same fate you may meet; So nev-er mix your grog too strong, But al-ways take it neat; But al-ways take it neat, But al-ways take it neat."

CHORUS

With a chip chop cherry chop Fol de rol riddle rop, Chip chop cherry chop Fol de rol ray, With a chip chop cherry chop Fol de rol rid-dle rop, Chip chop cher-ry chop Fol de rol ray.

BILLY BOY

Arr. RALPH GREAVES

BLACK-EYED SUSAN
(RICHARD LEVERIDGE, 1725?)

JOHN GAY

Arr. GERRARD WILLIAMS

BLOW AWAY THE MORNING DEW

Arr. KATHLEEN MARKWELL

Upon the sweet-est sum-mer-time, In the mid-dle of the morn, A
She gath-ered up her love-ly flowrs, And spent her time in sport; As
The yel-low cows-lip by the brim, The daff-o-dil as well, The
She's gone with all those flow-ers sweet, Of white, of red of blue, And

pret-ty dam-sel I es-pied, The fair-est ev-er born.
if in pret-ty Cu-pids bowers, She dai-ly did re-sort.
tim-id prim-rose, pale and trim, The pret-ty snow-drop bell.
un-to me a-bout my feet Is on-ly left the rue.

And sing blow a-way the

morn-ing dew, The dew and the dew, Blow a-way the morn-ing dew, How

All except last chorus

sweet the winds do blow.

Last chorus

sweet the winds do blow.

BLOW THE MAN DOWN

Arr. GERRARD WILLIAMS

THE BOAR'S HEAD CAROL

Arr. S. TAYLOR HARRIS

THE BOATMAN

Arr. S. TAYLOR HARRIS

BOBBY SHAFTOE

Arr. RALPH GREAVES

D.S.

BONNIE CHARLIE'S NOW AWA'

LADY NAIRNE

Arr. RALPH GREAVES

BONNIE DOON

BURNS

Arr. ERIC MAREO

BONNIE DUNDEE

WALTER SCOTT

Arr. RALPH GREAVES

In quick march time

SOLO

To the Lords of Con - ven - tion 'twas
There are hills be - yond Pent - land and
A - way to the caves, to the

Claver'se who spoke, "Ere the king's crown shall fall, there are crowns to be broke; Then each cav - a - lier who loves
lands be - yond Forth, If there's lords in the low - lands, there's chiefs in the North; There are wild Duin - ne - was - sals, three
hills, to the rocks, Ere I own a u - sur - per, I'll couch with the fox; And trem - ble, false knaves, in the

hon - our and me. Let him fol - low the bon - net of Bon - nie Dun - dee."
thousand times three, Will cry 'hoigh' for the bon - net of Bon - nie Dun - dee.
midst of your glee, You have not seen the last of my bon - net and me.

CHORUS

Come fill up my cup, come

fill up my can, come sad - dle your hors - es and call up your men; Come

o - pen the West Port, and let me gang free, And it's room for the bonnets of Bon - nie Dundee.

THE BRITISH GRENADIERS

Arr. GERRARD WILLIAM

CALENO CUSTURE ME

Arr. S. TAYLOR HARRIS

THE CAMPBELLS ARE COMIN'

Arr. RALPH GREAVES

CAMPTOWN RACES

(STEPHEN C. FOSTER.)

Arr. KATHLEEN MARKWELL

O CAN YE SEW CUSHIONS

Arr. S. TAYLOR HARRIS

CA' THE YOWES

Arr. S. TAYLOR HARRIS

CHARLIE IS MY DARLING

Arr. RALPH GREAVES

In rousing rhythm

SOLO

VOICE

PIANO

Char - lie is my dar - ling, my

dar - ling, my dar - ling, Char - lie is my dar - ling, the young chev - a - lier. 'Twas

on a Mon - day morn - ing, right ear - ly in the year, that Char - lie came to our town, The
he cam' marching up the street, The pipes play'd loud and clear; And a' the folk cam' rin - nin out, To
Hie - land bon - nets on their heads, And clay-mores bright and clear, They cam' to fight for Scot-land's right, And the
there were mon - y beat-ing hearts, And mon - y hopes and fears; And mon - y were the pray'rs put up For the

CHORUS

young chev - a - lier.
meet the chev - a - lier.
young chev - a - lier.
young chev - a - lier.

Oh! Char - lie is my dar - ling, my dar - ling, my dar - ling,

Verses 1 2 & 3 SOLO *Last Verse*

Char - lie is my dar - ling, the young chev - a - lier. As Wi' young chev - a - lier.
Oh,

CLEMENTINE
(PERCY MONTROSE)

Arr. KATHLEEN MARKWELL

SOLO

In a cav - ern, in a can - yon, Ex - ca -
Light she was and like a fai - ry, And her
Drove she duck - lings to the wa - ter, Ev - ery
Saw her lips a - bove the wa - ter Blow - ing

-vat - ing for a mine, Dwelt a min - er, for - ty nin - er, And his daugh - ter Clem - en - tine.
shoes were num - ber nine, Her-ring box - es with-out top - ses, Sandals were for Clem-en-tine.
morn - ing just at nine, Hit her foot a - gainst a splin - ter Fell in - to the foam-ing brine.
bub - bles might-y fine, But a - las! I was no swim - mer, So I lost my Clem-en-tine.

CHORUS

Oh my darl - ing, oh my darl - ing, oh my darl - ing Cle - men - tine! Thou art

lost and gone for ev - er, dread - ful sor - ry, Cle - men - tine!

5
SOLO Then the miner, forty niner,
    Soon began to peak and pine,
    Thought he oughter jine his daughter,
    Now he's with his Clementine.
      CHORUS Oh my darling etc.

6
SOLO In my dreams she still doth haunt me,
    Robed in garlands soaked in brine;
    Though in life I used to hug her,
    Now she's dead I draw the line.
      CHORUS Oh my darling etc.

7
SOLO How I missed her, how I missed her,
    How I missed my Clementine,
    But I kissed her little sister,
    And forgot my Clementine.
      CHORUS Oh my darling etc

THE CHESAPEKE AND SHANNON

Arr. GERRARD WILLIAMS

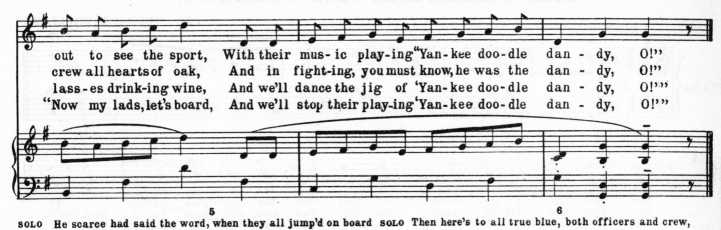

out to see the sport, With their mus-ic play-ing "Yan-kee doo-dle dan-dy, O!"
crew all hearts of oak, And in fight-ing, you must know, he was the dan-dy, O!"
lass-es drink-ing wine, And we'll dance the jig of 'Yan-kee doo-dle dan-dy, O!'"
"Now my lads, let's board, And we'll stop their play-ing 'Yan-kee doo-dle dan-dy, O!'"

5
SOLO He scarce had said the word, when they all jump'd on board
And they hauled down the ensign neat and handy, O!
Notwithstanding all their brag, the glorious British flag
At the Yankees' mizen-peak it looked the dandy, O!

CHORUS Yankee doodle etc.,

6
SOLO Then here's to all true blue, both officers and crew,
Who tamed the Yankees' courage neat and handy, O!
And may it ever prove in battle, as in love,
The true British sailor is the dandy, O!

CHORUS Yankee doodle etc.,

AT THE HALT, ON THE LEFT

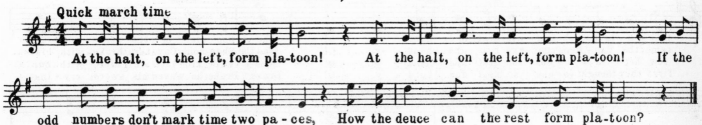

At the halt, on the left, form pla-toon! At the halt, on the left, form pla-toon! If the

odd numbers don't mark time two pa-ces, How the deuce can the rest form pla-toon?

MADEMOISELLE FROM ARMENTIÈRES

Par - lez-vous,

Par - lez-vous,

In - ky, pin - ky, Par - lez - vous.

PACK UP YOUR TROUBLES IN YOUR OLD KIT-BAG

Pack up your troubles in your old kit-bag,
And smile, smile, smile.
While you've a lucifer to light your fag,
Smile, boys, that's the style.
What's the use of worrying?
It never was worth while, so
Pack up your troubles in your old kit-bag
And smile, smile, smile.

COCKLES AND MUSSELS

At a moderate pace

Arr. ARCHIBALD JACOB

In Dub-lin's fair ci-ty, where girls are so pret-ty, I first set my eyes on sweet
She was a fish-monger, but sure 'twas no won-der, For so were her fath-er and
She died of a fev-er, and no one could save her, And that was the end of sweet

Mol-ly Ma-lone, As she wheel'd her wheel-bar-row through streets broad and nar-row, Cry-ing,
moth-er be-fore; And they each wheel'd their bar-row through streets broad and nar-row, Cry-ing,
Mol-ly Ma-lone; Her ghost wheels her bar-row through streets broad and nar-row, Cry-ing,

CHORUS

Coc-kles and Mus-sels! a-live, a-live oh!
Coc-kles and Mus-sels! a-live, a-live oh!
Coc-kles and Mus-sels! a-live, a-live oh!

A-live, a-live oh! A-

-live, a-live oh! Cry-ing Coc-kles and Mus-sels a-live, a-live oh!

COCK ROBIN
ARMY VERSION

Arr. KATHLEEN MARKWELL

SOLO

Who killed Cock Robin? "I" said the spar-row, "With my bow and ar-row, I killed Cock Robin."
Who saw him die? "I" said the fly, "With my lit-tle eye, I saw him die."
Who'll toll the bell? "I" said the bull, "Be-cause I can pull I'll toll the bell."
Who'll dig the grave? "I" said the owl, "With my lit-tle trowel I'll dig his grave."

CHORUS

All the birds in the air fell a - sigh-ing and a - sob-bing When they

heard of the death of poor Cock Robin, When they heard of the death of poor Cock Ro-bin.

Faster

John-ny will you go, John-ny will you go, John-ny will you go with an E I O?

John-ny will you go, John-ny will you go, John-ny will you go - i - o?

5
SOLO Who'll be the parson?
"I said the rook,
With my bell and book
I'll be the parson."
CHORUS **All the birds etc.**

6
SOLO Who'll be chief mourner?
"I said the dove,
I mourn for my love
I'll be chief mourner."
CHORUS **All the birds etc.**

COLD'S THE WIND

THOMAS DEKKER

Arr. S. TAYLOR HARRIS

Cold's the wind and wet's the rain, Saint Hugh be our good speed;
Troll the bowl, the nut brown bowl, And here kind mate to thee!

Ill is the wea-ther that brings no gain, Nor helps good hearts in need.
Let's sing a dirge for Saint Hugh's soul, And drown it mer-ri-ly.

Hey down-a-down Hey down-a-down Hey der-ry der-ry down-a-down,

Ho, well done, to me let come, Ring com-pass, gen-tle joy.

COME, HERE'S TO ROBIN HOOD

JOHN OXENFORD

Arr. S. TAYLOR HARRIS

COME, LANDLORD. FILL THE FLOWING BOWL.

Arr. ERIC MAREO

COME, LASSES AND LADS

Arr. GERRARD WILLIAMS

COME O'ER THE SEA

MOORE

Arr. S. TAYLOR HARRIS

COMIN' THRO' THE RYE

Arr. KATHLEEN MARKWELL

Gin a bo-dy meet a bo-dy, Com-in' thro' the rye;
Gin a bo-dy meet a bo-dy, Com-in' frae the toon,
A-mang the train there is a swain I dear-ly lo'e my-sel',

Gin a bo-dy kiss a bo-dy, Need a bo-dy cry?
Gin a bo-dy greet a bo-dy, Need a bo-dy froon?
But what's his name, or whar's his hame, I din-na care to tell.

Il-ka las-sie has her lad-die, Nane, they say, ha'e I, Yet

a' the lads they smile at me, When com-in' thro' the rye.

A COTTAGE WELL THATCHED WITH STRAW!

Arr. RALPH GREAVES

A COTTAGE WELL THATCHED WITH STRAW

cottage well thatch'd with straw. And a cottage well thatch'd with straw. For he had

home - brew'd, brown bread, and a cottage well thatch'd with straw.

OLD MACDOUGAL HAD A FARM

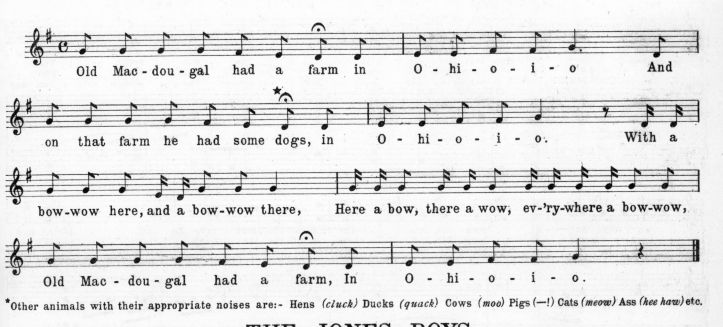

Old Mac-dou-gal had a farm in O-hi-o-i-o And

on that farm he had some dogs, in O-hi-o-i-o. With a

bow-wow here, and a bow-wow there, Here a bow, there a wow; ev'ry-where a bow-wow,

Old Mac-dou-gal had a farm, In O-hi-o-i-o.

*Other animals with their appropriate noises are:- Hens *(cluck)* Ducks *(quack)* Cows *(moo)* Pigs *(—!)* Cats *(meow)* Ass *(hee haw)* etc.

THE JONES BOYS

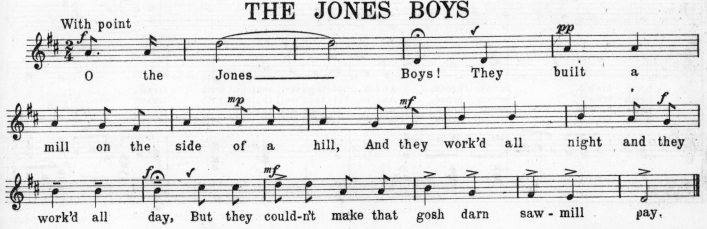

O the Jones Boys! They built a

mill on the side of a hill, And they work'd all night and they

work'd all day, But they could-n't make that gosh darn saw-mill pay.

COVENTRY CAROL

Arr. S. TAYLOR HARRIS

DAVID OF THE WHITE ROCK

Arr. HAROLD DAVIDSON

With deep feeling

PIANO

Da - vid— lay— dy - ing, his harp— by— his— side;
Da - vid— our— min - strel, we hear— thy— voice still,

"Sing, brave harp sing, though I fal - ter!" he— cried,
Those sweet sounds lin - ger— in val - ley— and— hill,

Faint his aged voice, but— his— spi - rit so strong,—
Thy brave heart beats in— the— songs that— we— sing,—

Moun - tains and— val - leys— all e - choed his song.
Through all— the— a - ges— that e - cho shall ring.

DOWN AMONG THE DEAD MEN

JOHN DYER.

Arr. RALPH GREAVES

DRINK TO ME ONLY WITH THINE EYES

BEN JONSON

Arr. RALPH GREAVES

THE DRUMMER AND THE COOK

Arr. GERRARD WILLIAMS

5. SOLO Sez the drummer to the cookie, "Will I buy the weddin' ring?"   6. SOLO Sez the drummer to the cookie, "Will ye name the weddin'day?"
   Sez the cookie, "Now you're talkin'. That would be the very thing."   Sez the cookie, "We'll be married in the merry month o' May."
CHORUS With her one eye etc.   CHORUS With her one eye etc.

7. SOLO When they went to church to say "I will," the drummer got a nark
For her one eye gliffed the Parson, and the t'other killed the Clerk.
CHORUS With her one eye etc.

EARLY ONE MORNING

Arr. RALPH GREAVES

Early one morning, just as the sun was ri - sing, I heard a maid
"Oh, gay is the gar - land, and fresh are the ro - ses, I've cull'd from the
"Re - mem - ber the_ vows that you made to your Ma - ry, Re - mem - ber the
Thus sang the poor maid - en, her sor - rows be - wail - ing, Thus sang the poor

sing___ in the val - ley be - low:
gar - den to bind on thy brow.
bow'r where you vow'd to be true.
maid___ in the val - ley be - low.

"O, don't de - ceive_ me!

O ne - ver leave me! How_ could you use a_ poor_ maid - en so?"

EARTH TO-DAY REJOICES

Dr. NEALE

Arr. S. TAYLOR HARRIS

FAITHFUL JOHNNY

Arr. S. TAYLOR HARRIS

FAREWELL TO FIUNARY

NORMAN McLEOD

Arr. ARCHIBALD JACOB

The wind is fair the day is fine And swift-ly, swift-ly
A thou-sand, thou-sand ten-der ties, A-wake this day my
With pen-sive steps I oft-en strolled, Where Fin-gal's cas-tle

runs the time The boat is float-ing on the tide That wafts us off from Fiu-na-ry.
plain-tive sighs, My heart with-in me al-most dies, To think of leav-ing Fiu-na-ry.
stood of old; And lis-tened while the shep-herd told The le-gend tales of Fiu-na-ry.

CHORUS

We must up and be a-way We must up and be a-way

We must up and be a-way Fare-well, fare-well to Fiu-na-ry.

THE FARMER'S BOY

Arr. KATHLEEN MARKWELL

THE FARMER'S DAUGHTERS

Arr. GERRARD WILLIAMS

5

SOLO So down the river the maiden swam,
  CHORUS Bow down, Bow down,
SOLO So down the river the maiden swam,
  Until she came to the miller's dam.
    CHORUS Singing etc.

6

SOLO The miller's daughter stood at the door,
  CHORUS Bow down, Bow down,
SOLO The miller's daughter stood at the door,
  Blooming like a gillyflower.
    CHORUS Singing etc.

7

SOLO "O Father, O Father, here comes a swan,
  CHORUS Bow down, Bow down,
SOLO "O Father, O Father, here comes a swan,
  Very much like a gentlewoman."
    CHORUS Singing etc.

8

SOLO The miller he took his rod and hook,
  CHORUS Bow down, Bow down,
SOLO The miller he took his rod and hook,
  And he fished the maiden out of the brook.
    CHORUS Singing etc.

FIRE DOWN BELOW

Arr. RALPH GREAVES

VOICE

PIANO

Fast and very loud

SOLO

Fire in the gal - ley, fire down be - low;____ It's
Fire in the fore - peak, fire down be - low;____ It's
Fire in the wind - lass, fire in the chain;____ It's
Fire up a - loft, and fire down be - low;____ It's

CHORUS

fetch a buck-et o' wa - ter, girls, there's fire down be - low.
fetch a buck-et o' wa - ter, girls, there's fire down be - low.
fetch a buck-et o' wa - ter, girls, and put it out a - gain.
fetch a buck-et o' wa - ter, girls, there's fire down be - low.

Fire, fire,

fire down be - low,____ It's fetch a buck-et o' wa - ter, girls, there's fire down be - low.

THE FROG AND THE MOUSE

Arr. KATHLEEN MARKWELL

THE GIRL I LEFT BEHIND ME

Arr. ERIC MAREO

In march time

PIANO

I'm lone-some since I cross'd the hill And o'er the moor and val - ley; Such
Oh! ne'er shall I for - get the night, The stars were bright a - bove me, And
Her gold - en hair, in ring-lets fair, Her eyes like dia - monds shin - ing, Her

hea - vy thoughts my heart do fill, Since part - ing with my Sal - ly. I
gent - ly lent their silv - 'ry light, When first she vow'd to love me. But
slen - der waist, with car - riage chaste May leave the swan re - pin - ing. Ye

seek no more the fine or gay, For each does but re - mind me How
now I'm bound to Brigh - ton camp; Kind Hea - ven, then pray guide me, And
gods a - bove: oh, hear my prayer, To my beau - teous fair to bind me, And

swift the hours did pass a - way, With the girl I left be - hind me.
bring me safe - ly back a - gain To the girl I left be - hind me.
send me safe - ly back a - gain To the girl I left be - hind me.

GOD BLESS THE PRINCE OF WALES

(BRINLEY RICHARDS)

Arr. ARCHIBALD JACOB

GOD REST YE MERRY, GENTLEMEN

Arr. RALPH GREAVES

GOD SAVE THE KING

Arr. GERRARD WILLIAMS.

GOLDEN SLUMBERS

Arr. GERRARD WILLIAMS

Gold - en slum - bers kiss your eyes, Smiles a - wake you when you rise; Sleep, pret - ty dar - ling, do not cry,— And I will sing a lul - la - by. - by.

Care— you know — not, there - fore sleep, While— I o'er you watch do keep;

THE GOLDEN VANITY

Arr. S. TAYLOR HARRIS

SOLO He bor'd with the augur, he bored once and twice,
   And some were playing cards, and some were playing dice,
   When the water flowed in it dazzled their eyes,
      As she sank by the Low-lands low.
CHO. By the Low-lands low etc.

SOLO Then the Cabin-boy did swim all to the starboard side
   Saying, Messmates take me in, I am drifting with the tide!
   Then they laid him on the deck, and he closed his eyes and died,
      As they sailed by the Low-lands low.
CHOR. By the Low-lands low etc.

GOOD KING WENCESLAS

Arr. ARCHIBALD JACOB

-las look'd out On the feast of Ste - phen, When the snow lay round a - bout;

Deep and crisp and e - ven; Bright-ly shone the moon that night, Though the frost was

cru - el, When a poor man came in sight Gath'ring win-ter fu - - el.

MALE VOICES "Hither page and stand by me,
If thou know'st it telling,
Yonder peasant, who is he?
Where and what his dwelling?"

FEMALE VOICES "Sire, he lives a good league hence,
Underneath the mountain,
Right against the forest fence;
By Saint Agnes' fountain."

MALE VOICES "Bring me flesh and bring me wine,
Bring me pine-logs hither;
Thou and I will see him dine
When we bear them thither."

ALL TOGETHER Page and Monarch, forth they went,
Forth they went together;
Through the rude wind's wild lament
And the bitter weather.

FEMALE VOICES "Sire, the night is darker now,
And the wind blows stronger;
Fails my heart, I know not how,
I can go no longer."

MALE VOICES "Mark my footsteps, good my page;
Tread thou in them boldly;
Thou shalt find the winter rage
Freeze thy blood less coldly."

ALL TOGETHER In his master's steps he trod,
Where the snow lay dinted;
Heat was in the very sod
Which the saint had printed.
Therefore, Christian men be sure,
Wealth or rank possessing,
Ye who now will bless the poor,
Shall yourselves find blessing.

GREEN GROW THE RASHES O

GOOD-NIGHT, LADIES!

Arr. KATHLEEN MARKWELL

Good - night, la - dies,— Good - night, la - dies,— Good - night, la - dies— We're going to leave you now.
Fare - well, la - dies,— Fare - well, la - dies,— Fare - well, la - dies— We're going to leave you now.
Sweet dreams, la - dies,— Sweet dreams, la - dies,— Sweet dreams, la - dies— We're going to leave you now.

Mer - ri - ly we roll a - long, roll a - long, roll a - long,

Mer - ri - ly we roll a - long, O'er the dark blue sea.

GREEN GROW THE RASHES O

ROBERT BURNS

Arr. RALPH GREAVES

THE HARP THAT ONCE

MOORE

Arr. GERRARD WILLIAMS

1 The
2 No

harp   that once through   Ta - ra's halls   Its   soul   of   mu - sic   shed;   Now   The
more   to chiefs and   la - dies bright   The   harp   of   Ta - ra   swells;   The

hangs   as mute   on   Ta - ra's walls   As   if   that   soul were   fled.   So
chord   a - lone   that   breaks the night   Its   tale   of   ru - in   tells;   Thus

sleeps   the pride   of   for - mer days,   So   glo - ry's thrill   is   o'er,   And
Free - dom now   so   sel - dom wakes;   The   on - ly   throb   she   gives   Is

hearts   that once   beat   high   for praise   Now   feel that   pulse   no   more.
when   some heart   in   dig - nant breaks   To   show that   still   she   lives.

HAUL AWAY JOE

Arr. S. TAYLOR HARRIS

VOICE

PIANO

In a swinging rhythm

mf

SOLO

Way, haul a - way,_____ we'll haul a - way the bow - lin?_____
Way, haul a - way,_____ the pack - et is a roll - ing.

CHORUS

f

Way, haul a - way,_____ we'll haul a - way, Joe.

f

SOLO — O once I had a nigger gel, and she was fat and lazy
CHORUS — Way, haul away, we'll haul away, Joe.

SOLO — Then I had a Spanish gel, she nearly druv' me crazy
CHORUS — Way, haul away, we'll haul away, Joe.

SOLO — King Louis was the King of France before the revolution
CHORUS — Way, haul away, we'll haul away, Joe.

SOLO — King Louis got his head cut off and spoiled his constitution.
CHORUS — Way, haul away, we'll haul away, Joe.

SOLO — When I was a little boy, and so my mother told me
CHORUS — Way, haul away, we'll haul away, Joe.

SOLO — That if I did'nt kiss the gals, my lips would all go mouldy
CHORUS — Way, haul away, we'll haul away, Joe.

SOLO *(ppp)* Way, haul away, we'll hang and haul together
CHORUS — Way, haul away, we'll haul away, Joe.

SOLO *(ppppp)* Way, haul away, we'll haul for better weather
CHORUS — Way, haul away, we'll haul away, Joe.

HEART OF OAK

(Dr. BOYCE)

Arr. ARCHIBALD JACOB

HERE'S A HEALTH UNTO HIS MAJESTY

Arr. RALPH GREAVES

HERE'S TO THE MAIDEN

R. B. SHERIDAN

Arr. RALPH GREAVES

HIGH GERMANY

Arr. KATHLEEN MARKWELL

Fairly fast

PIANO

O Pol - ly love, O Pol - ly, the rout has now be - gun, And
O Har - ry love, O Har - ry you heark-en what I say, My
A horse I'll buy you dap - ple grey and on it you shall ride, And
O no my love, it may - not be, I can - not with you ride, For
O cur - sed are the cru - el wars that ev - er they should rise, And

we must be a - march - ing at the beat - ing of the drum; Go
feet are all too ten - der I can - not march a - way; Be
all my heart's de - light will be, a - trot - ting at your side; We'll
I have here my child - ren dear, at home I must a - bide; But
out of mer - ry Eng - land press many a lad like - wise; They

dress your-self all in your best and come a - long with me, I'll take you to the
sides my dear-est Har - ry, tho' man and wife we be, How am I fit for
ride o'er moor and mountain high, and breathe the air so free, And jaun - ti - ly we'll
all my thoughts and man - y pray'rs shall be the while with thee, As thou dost fight Old
pressed my Har - ry from me as all my bro-thers three, And sent them to the

All except last

cru - el wars in High Ger - ma - ny.
cru - el wars in High Ger - ma - ny.
ride a-long in High Ger - ma - ny.
Eng-land's wars in High Ger - ma - ny.
cru - el wars in High Ger - ma -

Last time

-ny.

8

HOME SWEET HOME
(Sir HENRY BISHOP)

Arr. S. TAYLOR HARRIS

HO-RO, MY NUT BROWN MAIDEN

PROFESSOR BLACKIE

Arr. RALPH GREAVES

HULLABALOO BALAY

Arr. RALPH GREAVES

4

SOLO   Me father said "young man me boy,"
CHORUS   Hullabaloo balay! Hullabaloo balahbalay!
SOLO   To which he quickly made reply,
CHORUS   Hullabaloo balay!

5

SOLO   Next day while dad was in the "Crown,"
CHORUS   Hullabaloo balay! Hullabaloo balahbalay!
SOLO   Me mother ran off with Shallow Brown.
CHORUS   Hullabaloo balay!

LAST VERSE

SOLO   Me father slowly pined away,
CHORUS   Hullabaloo balay! Hullabaloo balahbalay!
SOLO   'Cause mother came back on the following day.
CHORUS   Hullabaloo balay, BALAY!

From 'Six Sea Shanties' (S. Taylor Harris) by permission of Messrs Boosey & Cº Ltd

I AM A BRISK AND SPRIGHTLY LAD

Arr. GERRARD WILLIAMS

I'LL BID MY HEART BE STILL

THOMAS PRINGLE

Arr GERRARD WILLIAMS

bid my heart be___ still, And___ check each strugg - ling
bid me cease to___ weep, For___ glo - ry gilds his
min - strels wake the___ lay, For___ peace and free - dom
cheek has lost its___ hue, My___ eye grows faint and

sigh! And there's none e'er shall know My soul's__ cher-ished woe, When the
name; Ah! 'tis there - fore I mourn He ne'er__ can re - turn To en -
won, Like my lost lov-er's knell The tones__ seem to swell, And I
dim, But 'tis sweet - er to fade, In grief's__ gloom-y shade, Than to

first___ tears of sor - row are dry.
joy___ the bright noon of his fame.
hear___ but his death - dirge a - lone.
bloom___ for an - oth - er than him.

I MARRIED A WIFE

Arr. S. TAYLOR HARRIS

THE ISLAND

DIBDIN

Arr. RALPH GREAVES

Briskly

SOLO

Dad - dy
Ju - lius
Then a
But —

Nep - tune one day— to Free-dom did say,— "If ev - er I liv'd up - on dry land, The
Cae - sar the Ro-man who yield-ed to no man, Came by wa - ter, he could-n't come by land! And
ve - ry great war-man, called Bil - ly the Nor-man, Cried "Hang it! I nev - er liked my land; It
par - ty de - ceit help'd the Nor-mans to beat,— Of trai-tors they man-aged to buy land; By Dane,

spot I would hit on would be lit - tle Brit-ain" Says Free-dom, "Why, that's my own Is - land."
Dane, Pict, and Sax - on, their homes turn'd their backs on, And all for the sake of our Is - land.
would be more han-dy to leave this Nor-man-dy, And live on yon beau-ti-ful Is - land." Says
Sax-on, or Pict,— we ne'er had been lick'd, Had they stuck to the King of their Is - land. Poor

CHORUS

Oh! what a snug lit - tle Is - land, A right lit - tle, tight lit - tle Is - land;
Oh! what a snug lit - tle Is - land, They'd all have a touch at the Is - land,
he "'Tis a snug lit - tle Is - land, Shan't us go and vis - it the Is - land?"
Har - old, the King of the Is - land, He lost both his life and his Is - land;

All the globe round, none can be found As hap-py as this lit-tle Is - land.
Some were shot dead-- some of them fled, And some stay'd to live on the Is - land.
Hop, skip and jump,-- There he was plump, And he kicked up a dust in the Is - land.
That's ve - ry true,-- What could he do? Like a Bri-ton he died for his Is - land.

5

SOLO Then the Spanish Armada set out to invade-a,
Quite sure if they ever came nigh land,
They couldn't do less than tuck up Queen Bess,
And take their full swing in the Island.
CHORUS Oh! the poor Queen and the Island,
The drones came to plunder the Island,
But snug in her hive, the Queen was alive,
And buzz was the word in the Island.

6

SOLO These proud puff'd-up cakes thought to make ducks and drakes
Of our wealth; but they scarcely could spy land,
Ere our Drake had the luck to make their pride duck
And stoop to the lads of the Island.
CHORUS The good wooden walls of the Island;
Huzza! for the lads of the Island;
Devil or Don, let them come on,
But how'd they come off at the Island!

7

SOLO I don't wonder much that the French and the Dutch
Have since oft been tempted to try land,
And I wonder much less they have met no success,
For why should we give up our Island?
CHORUS Oh! 'tis a wonderful Island,
All of 'em long for the Island;
Hold a bit there, let 'em take fire and air,
But we'll have the sea and the Island.

8

SOLO Then since Freedom and Neptune have hitherto kept tune
In each saying "This shall be my land;"
Should the "Army of England", or all it could bring, land
We'd show 'em some play for the Island.
CHORUS We'd fight for our right to the Island,
We'd give them enough of the Island;
Invaders should just— bite at the dust,
But not a bit more of the Island.

NON NOBIS DOMINE

WILLIAM BYRD

Non no-bis Do - mi - ne, non no - bis; sed no-mi-ni tu - o da
Non no-bis Do - mi - ne, non no - bis; sed no-mi-ni tu -
Non no-bis Do - mi - ne, non no - bis; sed

glo - ri - am; sed no-mi-ni tu - o da glo - ri - am Non no-bis Do - mi-
o da glo - ri - am; sed no-mi-ni tu - o da glo - ri - am Non no-bis
no-mi-ni tu - o da glo - ri - am; sed no-mi-ni tu - o da glo - ri - am.

I'SE GWINE BACK TO DIXIE

(C. A. WHITE)

Arr. KATHLEEN MARKWELL

JOHN BROWN'S BODY

With strength and swinging rhythm

Arr. KATHLEEN MARKWELL

PIANO

SOLO
John Brown's bo-dy lies a mould'ring in the grave, John Brown's bo-dy lies a mould'ring in the grave,
The stars of hea - ven are look-ing kind-ly down, The stars of hea - ven are look-ing kind-ly down,
He's gone to be a soldier in the ar-my of the Lord, He's gone to be a sol-dier in the ar-my of the Lord,

John Brown's bo - dy lies a mould-'ring in the grave, But his soul goes march-ing on.
The stars of hea - ven are look-ing kind-ly down, On the grave of Old John Brown.
He's gone to be a sol-dier in the ar - my of the Lord, And his soul goes march-ing on.

CHORUS
Glo - ry, glo-ry, Hal-le-lu - jah! Glo - ry, glo-ry, Hal-le-lu - jah!

Glo - ry, glo-ry, Hal-le-lu - jah! His soul goes marching on!

All except last Chorus | *Last time*

on!

JOHNNY COME DOWN TO HILO

Arr. RALPH GREAVES

JOHN PEEL

Arr. RALPH GREAVES

KING ARTHUR'S MEN

Arr. RALPH GREAVE

Briskly

PIANO

SOLO

King Ar-thur had__ three sons, that he had; King Ar-thur had three
The first he was__ a__ mil-ler, that he was; The sec-ond he was a
Now the mil-ler stole some grist__ for his mill that he did; And the weav-er stole some wool for his
Oh, the mil-ler he was drowned in his__ dam, that he was; And the weav-er he was killed at his

sons, that he had; He had three sons of yore, and he kick'd them out of door, Be
weav-er, that he was; And the third__ he__ was a__ lit-tle tail-or boy, And
loom, that he did; And the lit-tle tail-or boy, he__ stole some cord-er-oy, For to
loom, that he was; And Old Nick he cut his stick with the lit-tle tail-or boy, With the

CHORUS

-cause they could not sing, that he did. Be-cause they could not__ sing, that he did; Be
he was migh-ty clev-er, that he was. And he was migh-ty__ clev-er, that he was; And
keep those three rogues warm, that he did. For to keep those three rogues warm, that he did; For to
broad-cloth un-der his arm, that he did. With the broad-cloth under his__ arm, that he did; With the

-cause they could not__ sing, that he did; He had three sons of yore, and he
he was migh-ty__ clev-er, that he was; And the third__ he__ was, a__
keep those three rogues warm, that he did; And the lit-tle tail-or boy, he__
broad-cloth un-der his__ arm, that he did; And Old Nick he cut his stick with the

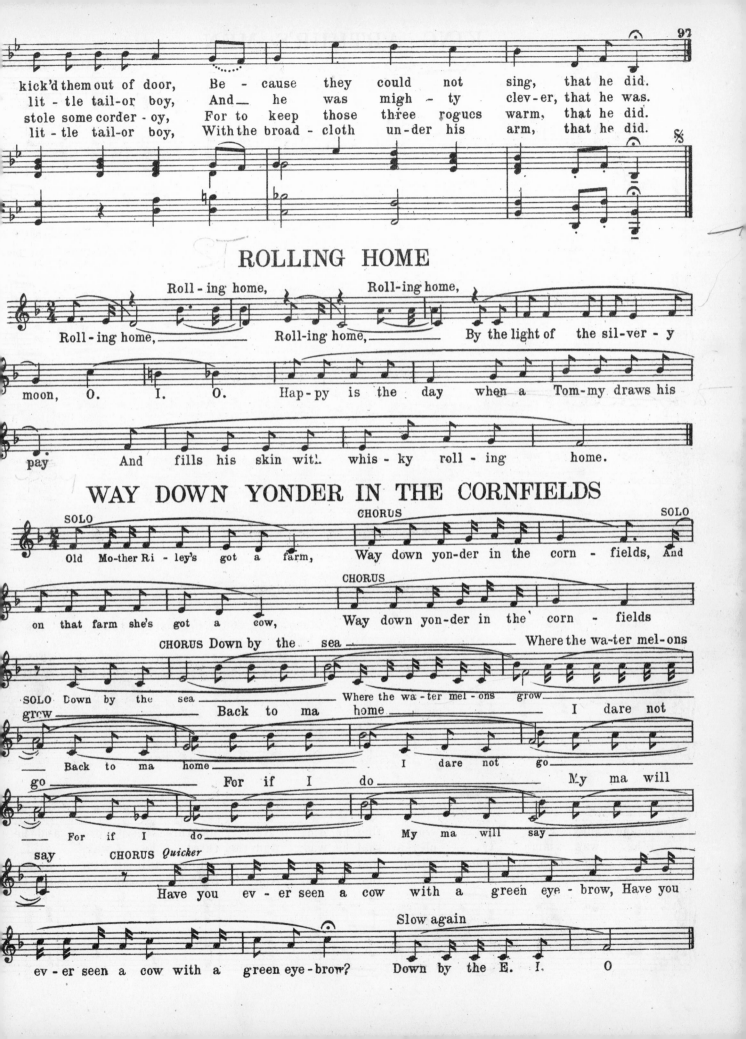

THE KEEL ROW

Arr. ERIC MAF

LAND OF MY FATHERS

(JAMES JAMES)

Arr. HAROLD DAVIDSON

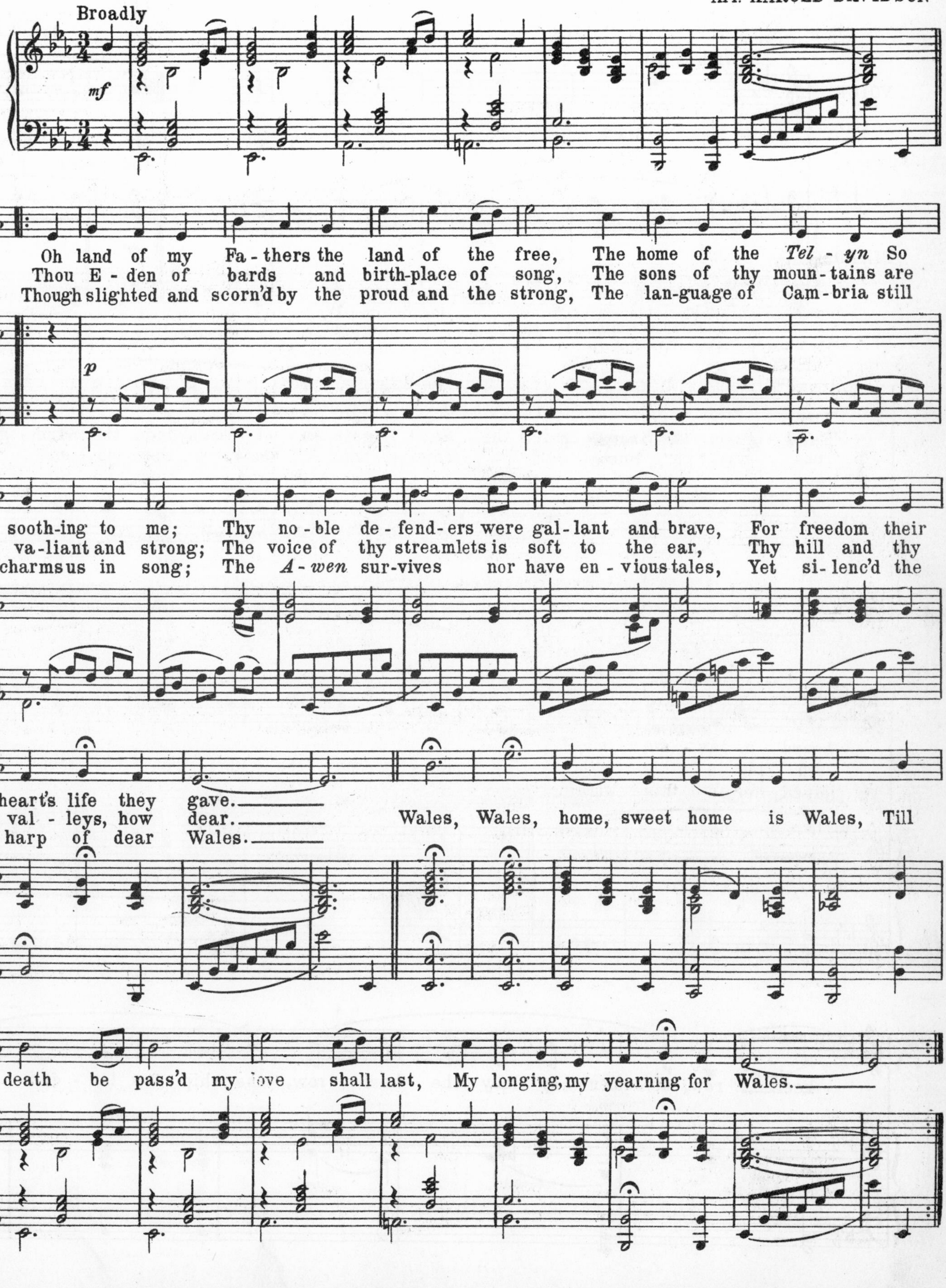
Broadly
PIANO
mf
p
Oh land of my Fa - thers the land of the free, The home of the Tel - yn So
Thou E - den of bards and birth-place of song, The sons of thy moun-tains are
Though slighted and scorn'd by the proud and the strong, The lan-guage of Cam-bria still
sooth-ing to me; Thy no - ble de - fend - ers were gal - lant and brave, For freedom their
va - liant and strong; The voice of thy streamlets is soft to the ear, Thy hill and thy
charms us in song; The A - wen sur - vives nor have en - vious tales, Yet si - lenc'd the
heart's life they gave.
val - leys, how dear.
harp of dear Wales.
Wales, Wales, home, sweet home is Wales, Till
death be pass'd my love shall last, My longing, my yearning for Wales.

THE LASS OF RICHMOND HILL
(J. HOOK)

Arr. ARCHIBALD JACOB

THE LASS THAT LOVES A SAILOR
(DIBDIN)

Arr. GERRARD WILLIAMS

THE LAST LONG MILE

Arr. RALPH GREAVES

not the load on the hard straight road that drives a - way your smile, If the
not the tramp nor the echoes of the camp that drives a - way your smile, It's the

socks of sis - ter raise a blis - ter, Blame it on the last long mile.
ser - geant - maj - or's lit - tle wag - er, To beat you on the last long mile.

AND WHEN I DIE

(CHORUS) And when I die, Don't bur-y me at
(SOLO) And when I die, Don't bur-y me at all;

all; Just pic-kle my bones, In al - co -
Just pic-kle my bones, In al - co - hol;

-hol; Put a bot-tle of booze, At my head and my
Put a bot-tle of booze, At my head and my feet

feet And then I know my bones will keep.
And then I know my bones will keep.

APRÈS LA GUERRE FINI

A - près la guerre fi - ni___ We'll go home to Blight - y.___
A - près la guerre fi - ni___ En-glish sol - dier par - ti.___
Lorsque la guerre fi - ni___ Sol-dat An - glais par - ti.___

Wont we be sor-ry to leave chére Ger - maine A - près la guerre fi - ni.
Mam'selle Fran-cais beaucoup pic-an-ni - ny A - près la guerre fi - ni.
Na - poo bul - ly beef com-me sou-ven - ie Ma-dame, your soup's no bonne.

THE LAST ROSE OF SUMMER

MOORE

ERIC MARK

THE LEATHER BOTTEL

Arr S. TAYLOR HARRIS

With strength

VOICE

PIANO

mf

When I sur-vey_ the
Now, what do you say to these
Then what do you say to these
And when the bottle at

world a-round, The won - drous things that do a-bound, The ships that on the
cans of wood? Oh no, in faith they can't be good, For if the bear - er
glass - es fine? Oh, they shall have no praise of mine, For if you chance to
last grows old And will good liquor no long - er hold, Out of the sides you may

sea_ do swim, To keep out foes that none come in; Well! let them all_ say
fall by the way, Why, on the ground your liquor doth lay: But had it been in a
touch the brim, Down falls the liquor and all there - in; But had it been in a
make a clout, To mend your shoes when they're worn out; Or_ take and hang it up

what they can, 'Twas for one end— the use of man. So I wish him joy wher -
leather bot - tel, Although he had fall - en, all had been well. So I wish him joy wher -
leather bot - tel, And the stop - per in, all had been well. So I wish him joy wher -
on a pin, 'Twill serve to put hing-es and odd things in. So I wish him joy wher -

- e'er he dwell, That first found out_ the lea - ther bot - tel._
- e'er he dwell, That first found out_ the lea - ther bot - tel._
- e'er he dwell, That first found out_ the lea - ther bot - tel._
- e'er he dwell, That first found out_ the lea - ther bot - tel._

8

LET BUCKS A-HUNTING GO

Arr. S. TAYLOR HARRIS

LILLIBURLERO

Arr. S. TAYLOR HARRIS

In strict march time

PIANO

SOLO

Ho bro-ther Teague dost hear the de-cree
O by my soul it is the Tal-bot
And the good Tal-bot is made a lord
Now the good Tal-bot is com-ing a-shore

CHORUS

Lil-li-bur-le - ro bul-len a la

SOLO

Dat we shall have a new dep-u-tie
And he will cut all the trai-tors throat
And he with brave lads is com-ing a-board
And we shall have com-miss-ions gil-lore

CHORUS

Lil-li-bur-le - ro bul-len a la

Le - ro le - ro Lil-li-bur-le - ro Lil-li-bur-le - ro bul-len a la

Le - ro le - ro le - ro le - ro Lil-li-bur-le - ro bul-len a la

SOLO   There was an old prophecy found in a bog
CHORUS   **Lilliburlero bullen a la**
SOLO   That we should be ruled by an ass and a hog
CHORUS   { **Lilliburlero bullen a la**
   Lero lero, Lilliburlero *(etc.)*

SOLO   The prophecy's true and now come to pass
CHORUS   **Lilliburlero bullen a la**
SOLO   For Talbot's the hog and James is the ass
CHORUS   { **Lilliburlero bullen a la**
   Lero lero, Lilliburlero *(etc.)*

THE LINCOLNSHIRE POACHER

Arr. ARCHIBALD JACOB

When I was bound ap-pren—tice, in fam-ous Lin-coln-shire, Full
As me and my com-pan—ions were set—ting of a snare, 'Twas
As me and my com-pan—ions were set—ting four or five, And
I threw him on my shoul—der, and then we trudg—ed home, We
Suc-cess to ev-'ry gen-tle-man that lives in Lin-coln-shire, Suc

well I serv'd my mas-ter for more than sev-en year, Till
then we spied the game-keep-er, for him we did not care, For
tak-ing on 'em up a-gain, we caught a hare a-live, We
took him to a neigh-bour's house and sold him for a crown, We
-cess to ev-'ry poach-er that wants to sell a hare, Bad

I took up to poach-ing, as you shall quick-ly hear;
we can wrestle and fight, my boys, and jump o'er an-y-where.
took the hare a-live, my boys, and through the woods did steer. Oh, 'tis
sold him for a crown, my boys but, I did not tell you where.
luck to ev-'ry game-keep-er that will not sell his deer.

my de-light on a shin-ing night in the sea-son of the year.

THE LITTLE BROWN JUG

(R. A. EASTBURN)

Arr. ERIC MAREO

Bucolically

mf

SOLO

mf

My wife and I liv'd all a - lone, In a lit-tle log - hut we call'd our own;
When I go toil - ing to my farm I take little brown jug under my arm; I
If I'd a cow that gave such milk I'd clothe her in the fi - nest silk; I'd
The rose is red, my nose is too. The vi - o - lets blue and so are you; And

She lov'd gin and I lov'd rum — I tell you what, we'd lots of fun.
place it un-der a sha - dy tree — Lit-tle brown jug 'tis you and me.
feed her on the choi - cest hay And milk her for - ty times a day.
yet I guess, be - fore I stop, We'd bet - ter take a - no - ther drop.

CHORUS

Ha - ha - ha, you and me Lit-tle brown jug, don't I love thee

Ha - ha - ha, you and me Lit-tle brown jug, don't I love thee

LOCH LOMOND

Arr. RALPH GREAV

LOWLANDS

Arr. S. TAYLOR HARRIS

3.

SOLO   And bravely in her bosom fair.
CHORUS   **Lowlands, Lowlands away my John.**
SOLO   A red red rose my love did wear.
CHORUS   **My Lowlands away.**

4.

SOLO   She made no sound no word she said.
CHORUS   **Lowlands, Lowlands away my John.**
SOLO   And then I knew my love was dead.
CHORUS   **My Lowlands away.**

THE LONDONDERRY AIR

Arr KATHLEEN MARKWELL

O qui-et

rest   the dark-ling vales of   sor - row,__ O soft-ly sleep   the storm-y hills of
shine   the moun-tain tops of   glo - ry,__ O qui-et gleam   the hap - py fields of

pain____   The way they go   who have no more to - mor - row, And turn   not__
love____   The way they go   who have no more a   stor - ry, And weep   no__

back____   to look up-on their kind   a - gain. But O to wake   and feel the wind a-
more   to wake and find the stars   a - bove. But O to hear   the bus-y sea-birds

blow - ing____   A-cross the sea   from that too dis-tant   shore,__   To know the
cry - ing____   Last calls of home   that rend me ere we   part, ____   O were that

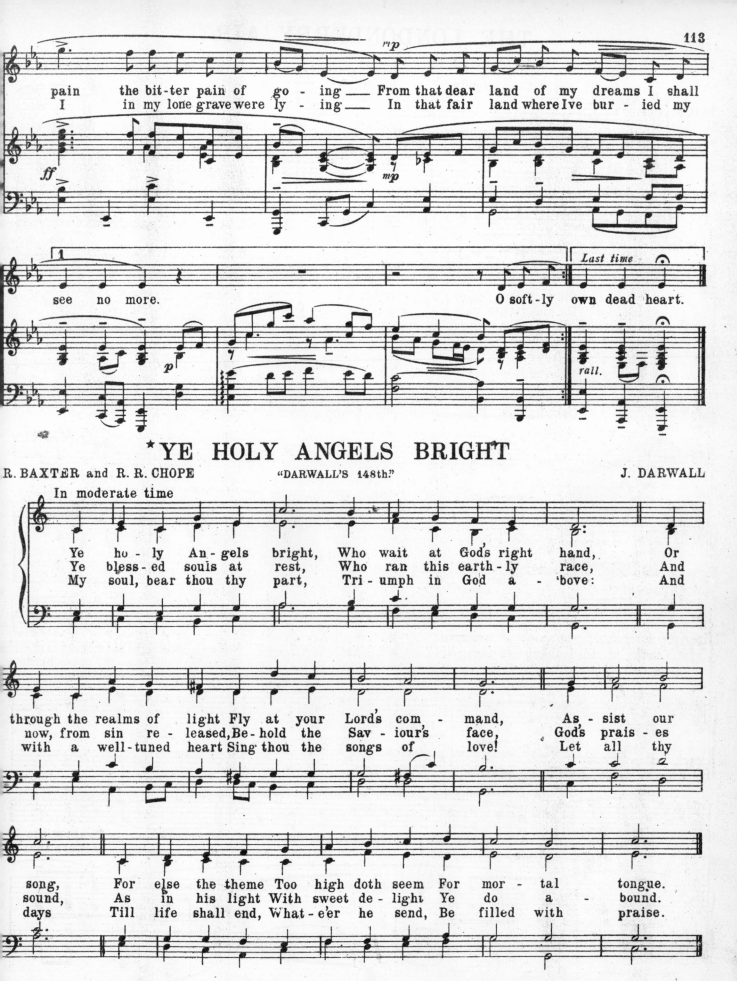

pain   the bit-ter pain of   go — ing ___ From that dear land of my dreams I shall
I   in my lone grave were ly — ing ___ In that fair   land where I've bur - ied my

see   no   more.   O soft-ly   own dead heart.

*YE HOLY ANGELS BRIGHT

R. BAXTER and R. R. CHOPE   "DARWALL'S 148th."   J. DARWALL

In moderate time

Ye   ho — ly   An - gels   bright,   Who wait   at God's right   hand,   Or
Ye   bless — ed   souls at   rest,   Who ran   this earth - ly   race,   And
My   soul, bear thou thy   part,   Tri — umph   in God a — bove: And

through the realms of   light Fly   at   your   Lord's com — mand,   As - sist   our
now, from sin re — leased, Be - hold   the   Sav — iour's   face,   God's prais - es
with   a   well-tuned   heart Sing thou the   songs   of   love!   Let   all   thy

song,   For   else   the theme Too high doth   seem For mor — tal   tongue.
sound,   As   in   his light With sweet de - light Ye   do   a — bound.
days   Till   life shall end, What - e'er he   send, Be   filled   with   praise.

From "The English Hymnal"

MARCHING THROUGH GEORGIA

(H.C.WORK)

Arr. RALPH GREAVES

Left Right, Left!

SOLO

Bring the good old bu-gle, boys, we'll sing an-o-ther song;
How the darkies shouted when they heard the joyful sound,
Yes, and there were "Union" men who wept with joyful tears,
So we made a thor-oughfare for free-dom and her train,

Sing it with a spi-rit that will start the world a - long!
How the turkeys gobbled which our commiss-a - ry found,
When they saw the honour'd flag they had not seen for years,
Six - ty miles in lat - i-tude, three hun-dred to the main,

Sing it as we us'd to sing it fif-ty thousand strong!
How the sweet po-ta - toes ev - en started from the ground,
Hard-ly could they be restrained from breaking forth in cheers,
Treason fled be-fore us, for re - sis-tance was in vain,

While we were march-ing thro' Georg - ia.
While we were march-ing thro' Georg - ia.
While we were march-ing thro' Georg - ia.
While we were march-ing thro' Georg - ia.

CHORUS

Hur - rah! Hur-rah! We bring the Ju-bi-lee! Hur-

-rah! Hur - rah! the flag that makes you free! So we sang the chor-us from At-

-lan - ta to the sea! While we were march-ing thro' Georg - ia!

D.C.

THE MARCH OF THE MEN OF HARLECH

THOMAS OLIPHANT

Arr. ERIC MAREO

In firm march time

1 { Hark! I hear the foe ad - vanc - ing, Barb - ed steeds are proud - ly pranc - ing;
Men of Har - lech lie ye dream - ing? See ye not their fal - chions gleam - ing,

2 { 'Mid the fray, see dead and dy - ing, Friend and foe to - geth - er ly - ing;
Fright - en'd steeds are wild - ly neigh - ing, Braz - en trum - pets hoarse - ly bray - ing,

repeat

Hel - mets, in the sunbeams glancing, Glit - ter through the trees.
While their pen - nons gai - ly streaming Flut - ter in the breeze?
All a - round the ar - rows fly - ing Scat - ter sud - den death!
Wound - ed men for mer - cy pray - ing With their part - ing breath!

From the rocks re - bounding
See - they're in dis - or - der! -

Let the war - cry sound - ing
Com - rades, keep close or - der!

Sum - mon all At Cam - bria's call, The haughty - foe sur -
Ev - er they Shall rue the day They ventured o'er the

- round - ing
bor - der!

Men of Har - lech, on to glo - ry! See, your ban - ner fam'd in sto - ry
Now the Sax - on flees be - fore us; Vic - tory's ban - ner float - eth o'er us!

ff

Waves these burn - ing words be - fore ye, "Bri - tain scorns to yield!"
Raise the loud, ex - ult - ing chor - us, "Bri - tain wins the field!"

MASSA'S IN DE COLD, COLD GROUND

(STEPHEN C. FOSTER)

Arr. S. TAYLOR HARRIS

Sadly and fairly slowly

THE MEETING OF THE WATERS

OORE

Arr. KATHLEEN MARKWELL

Tenderly, but not too slowly

There is not in the wide world a val - ley so sweet. As that
Yet it was not that na - ture had shed o'er the scene, Her
'Twas that friends the be - loved of my bo - som were near, Who made

vale in whose bo - som the bright wa - ters meet; O the last rays of feel - ing and
pur - est of crys - tal and bright-est of green, 'Twas not her soft mag - ic of
ev - 'ry dear scene of en - chant-ment more dear, And who felt how the best charms of

life must de - part, Ere the bloom of that val - ley shall fade from my heart, Ere the
stream-let or hill, O no! it was some-thing more ex - quis - ite still, O
na - ture im - prove, When we see them re - flect - ed from looks that we love, When we

End of last verse

bloom of that val-ley shall fade from my heart.
no! it was something more ex-quis-ite still.
see them re-flect-ed from looks that we love.

THE MERMAID

Arr. ERIC MAREO

SOLO Then up spoke the captain of our gallant ship
And a well-spoken captain was he,
"For the loss of our long boat we all shall be lost,
And go to the bottom of the sea."
CHORUS For the raging seas did roar. etc.

SOLO Then up spoke the mate so sturdy for to view,
And a well-spoken mate was he,
"I've married a wife in fair London Town,
And to-night she will weep for me."
CHORUS For the raging seas did roar. etc.

SOLO Then up spoke the cook with his ladle in his hand
And a well-spoken cook was he,
"I care no more for the pots and pans
Than I do for the galleys of the sea."
CHORUS For the raging seas did roar. etc.

SOLO Then three times round went our gallant ship,
And three times round went she,
And she gave one whirl, and she gave one twirl,
As she sank to the bottom of the sea.
CHORUS For the raging seas did roar. etc.

THE MILLER OF THE DEE

Arr. ARCHIBALD JACOB

There was a jol - ly mil - ler once Lived on the riv - er Dee;___ He
I live by my mill, she is to me Like par - ent, child and wife;___ I
Thus, like the mil - ler, bold and free, Let us re - joice and sing;___ The

worked and sang from morn till night, No lark as blithe as he.___ And
would not change my sta - tion For a - ny o - ther in life.___ No
days of youth are made for glee, And time is on the wing.___ This

this the bur - den of his song For ev - er used to be___ "I
law - yer, surgeon, or doc - tor, E'er had a groat from me___ "I
song shall pass from me to thee, A - long this jo - vial ring___ Let

care for no - bo - dy, no, not I, If no - bo - dy cares for me."___
care for no - bo - dy, no, not I, If no - bo - dy cares for me."___
heart and voice and all a - gree To say "Long live the King."___

THE MINSTREL BOY

Arr. ARCHIBALD JACOB

The Min-strel Boy to the war is gone In the ranks of death you'll find him; His
The Min-strel fell! but the foe - man's chain Could not bring his proud soul un - der; The

fa - ther's sword he has gird - ed on, And his wild harp slung be - hind him—
harp he loved ne'er spoke a - gain, For he tore its chords a - sun - der; And

"Land of song!" said the war-rior - bard, "Though all the world be - trays thee, One
said, "No chains shall sul - ly thee, Thou soul of love and brav - er - y! Thy

sword, at least, thy rights shall guard, One faith - ful harp shall praise thee"
songs were made for the pure and free, They shall nev - er sound in slave - ry"

MY BONNIE

Arr. KATHLEEN MARKWELL

MY OLD KENTUCKY HOME

(STEPHEN C. FOSTER)

Arr. ARCHIBALD JACOB

The sun shines bright in the old Kentuck-y home, 'Tis summer, the darkies are gay; The
They hunt no more for the 'pos-sum and the coon, On the meadow, the hill and the shore; They

corn-top's ripe and the mea-dow's in the bloom, While the birds make music all the day; The
sing no more by the glimmer of the moon, On the bench by the old cab-in door; The

young folks roll on the lit-tle cab-in floor, All mer-ry, all hap-py and bright; By'n-
day goes by like a sha-dow o'er the heart, With sor-row where all was de-light; The

bye hard times come a-knock-ing at the door, Then my old Kentuck-y home, good night.
time has come when the dark-ies have to part, Then my old Kentuck-y home, good night.

colla
voce

mf CHORUS

Weep no more, my la-dy, O weep no more to-day! We will

sing one song for the old Kentucky home, For the old Kentucky home, far a - way. *Repeat Chorus*

JESU, LOVER OF MY SOUL

"ABERYSTWYTH"

C. WESLEY   JOSEPH PARRY

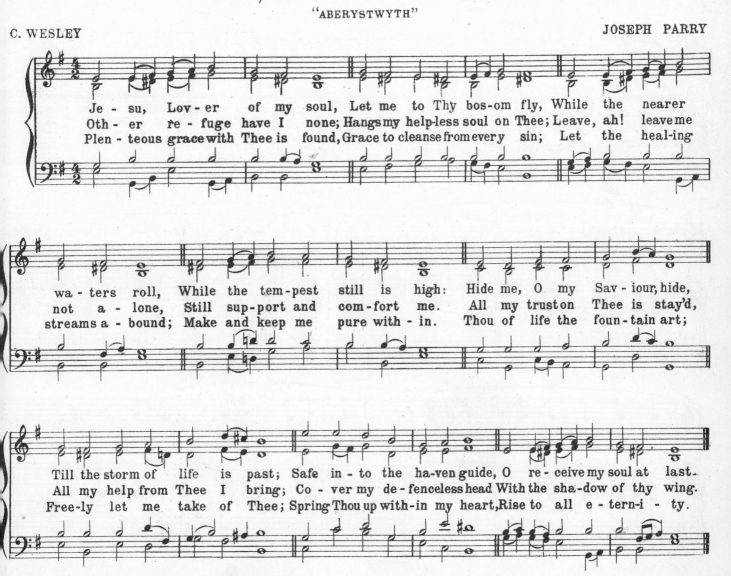

Je - su, Lov - er of my soul, Let me to Thy bos-om fly, While the nearer
Oth - er re - fuge have I none; Hangs my help-less soul on Thee; Leave, ah! leave me
Plen - teous grace with Thee is found, Grace to cleanse from every sin; Let the heal-ing

wa - ters roll, While the tem-pest still is high: Hide me, O my Sav - iour, hide,
not a - lone, Still sup-port and com-fort me. All my trust on Thee is stay'd,
streams a - bound; Make and keep me pure with - in. Thou of life the foun-tain art;

Till the storm of life is past; Safe in - to the ha-ven guide, O re - ceive my soul at last.
All my help from Thee I bring; Co - ver my de - fenceless head With the sha-dow of thy wing.
Free-ly let me take of Thee; Spring Thou up with-in my heart, Rise to all e - tern-i - ty.

By permission of Messrs Hughes & Son Wrexham

NEW YEAR'S NIGHT

Arr. GERRARD WILLIAMS

O THE OAK AND THE ASH

Arr. ARCHIBALD JACOB

A north country maid up to London had stray'd, Although with her nature it
While sadly I roam, I regret my dear home, Where lads and young lasses are
No doubt, did I please, I could marry with ease, Where maidens are fair, many

did not agree; She wept and she sigh'd, And she bitterly cried, I
making the hay; The bells they do ring, and the birds they do sing, And the
lovers will come; But he whom I wed must be north-country bred, And

wish once again in the north I could be.
fields and the gardens so pleasant and gay.
carry me back to my north-country home.

CHORUS

Oh! the oak and the ash and the bonny ivy tree, They flourish at home in my own country.

*O COME, ALL YE FAITHFUL
"ADESTE FIDELES"

5.
Child, for us sinners
Poor and in the manger,
Fain we embrace thee, with awe and love,
Who would not love thee
Loving us so dearly
   O come, let us adore him, etc.

6.
Sing, choirs of Angels,
Sing in exultation,
Sing, all ye citizens of heaven above;
Glory to God
In the Highest:
   O come, let us adore him, etc.

7.
Yea, Lord, we greet thee,
Born this happy morning,
Jesu, to thee be glory given;
Word of the Father,
Now in flesh appearing:
   O come, let us adore him, etc.

* From "The English Hymnal"

* O FAITH OF ENGLAND
"PSALM 68"

T.A.L.

M. GREITER

In moderate time, very dignified

O Faith of Eng-land, taught of old By faith-ful shep-herds of the
Our fa-thers heard the trum-pet call Thro' low-ly cot and king-ly
Our fa-thers held the faith re-ceived, By Saints de-clared, by Saints be-
Though fre-quent be the loud a-larms, Though still we march by ambushed

fold, The hallowing of our na-tion;_____ Thou wast thro' many a weal-thy year,
hall From o-ver-sea re-sound-ing;_____ They bowed their stub-born wills to learn
-lieved, By Saints in death de-fend-ed;_____ Thro' pain of doubt and bit-ter-ness,
arms Of death and hell sur-round-ed;_____ With Christ for chief we fear no foe,

Thro' many a dark-ened day of fear The rock of our sal-va-tion;_____
The truths that live, the thoughts that burn, With new re-solve a-bound-ing;_____
Thro' pain of trea-son and dis-tress, They for the right con-tend-ed;_____
Nor force nor craft can o-ver-throw The Church that he has found-ed;_____

A-rise, a-rise, good Chris-tian men, Your glo-rious stan-dard raise a-gain The
A-rise, a-rise, good Chris-tian men, Your glo-rious stan-dard raise a-gain The
A-rise, a-rise, good Chris-tian men, Your glo-rious stan-dard raise a-gain The
A-rise, a-rise, good Chris-tian men, Your glo-rious stan-dard raise a-gain The

Cross of Christ who calls you;_____ Who bids you live and bids you die
Cross of Christ who guides you;_____ Whose arm is bared to join the fray,
Cross of Christ who bought you;_____ Who leads you forth in this new age
Cross wherewith he signed you;_____ The King him-self shall lead you on,

For his great cause and stands on high To wit-ness what be-falls you.
Who mar-shalls you in stern ar-ray, Fear-less, what-e'er be-tides you.
With long-en-dur-ing hearts to wage The war-fare he has taught you.
Shall watch you till the strife be done, Then near his throne shall find you.

OFT IN THE STILLY NIGHT

MOORE

Arr. ARCHIBALD JACOB

OLD BLACK JOE
(STEPHEN C. FOSTER)

Arr. ARCHIBALD JACOB

Very sadly, but keep moving

PIANO

SOLO

Gone   are the days   when my heart was young and gay;   Gone   are my friends   from the
Why   do I weep   when my heart should feel no pain?   Why   do I sigh   that my
Where   are the hearts   once so hap-py and so free?   The child-ren so dear   that I

cot-ton fields a-way;   Gone   from the earth   to a bet-ter land I know,   I
friends come not a-gain?   Griev-ing   for forms   now de-part-ed long a-go,   I
held up-on my knee?   Gone   to the shore   where my soul has longed to go,   I

hear their gen-tle voic-es call-ing "Old Black Joe!"
hear their gen-tle voic-es call-ing "Old Black Joe!"
hear their gen-tle voic-es call-ing "Old Black Joe!"

CHORUS

I'm com-ing, I'm com-ing, For my

head is bend-ing low;   I   hear their gen-tle voic-es Call-ing "Old Black Joe!"

DE OLD FOLKS AT HOME

(STEPHEN C. FOSTER)

Arr. KATHLEEN MARKWELL

OLD KING COLE

Arr. S. TAYLOR HARRIS

SOLO Old King Cole was a merry old soul,
And a merry old soul was he,
He called for his pipe and he called for his bowl,
And he called for his harpers three.
Ev'ry harper he had a fine harp,
And a very fine harp had he.

CHOR. Then fiddle-diddle dee, fiddle dee went the fiddlers
Tootle-tootle-too, tootle-too went the pipers,
Twang-a-twang-a-twang, twang-a-twang went the harpers,
Merry men are we etc.

SOLO Old King Cole was a merry old soul,
And a merry old soul was he,
He called for his pipe and he called for his bowl,
And he called for his drummers three,
Ev'ry drummer he had a fine drum,
And a very fine drum had he.

CHOR. Then fiddle-diddle dee, fiddle dee went the fiddlers
Tootle-tootle-too, tootle-too went the pipers,
Twang-a-twang-a-twang, twang-a-twang went the
harpers,
Rub-a-dub-a-dub, rub-a-dub went the drummers,
Merry men are we etc.

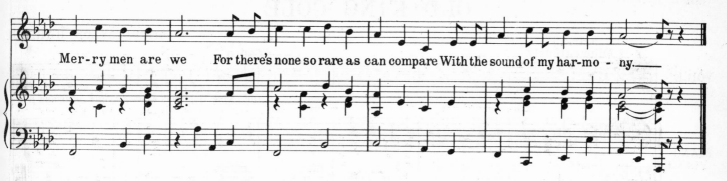

Mer-ry men are we   For there's none so rare as can compare With the sound of my har-mo - ny.____

(ARMY VERSION)

Old King Cole was a merry old soul,
  And a merry old soul was he,
He called for his pipe, and he called for his bowl,
  And he called for his Privates three.
Now every Private had a great thirst,
  And a very great thirst had he,
"Beer! Beer! Beer!" said the Private,
  For merry men are we,
And there's none so fair as can compare
  With the boys of the AR-R-MY.

Old King Cole was a merry old soul,
  And a merry old soul was he,
He called for his pipe, and he called for his bowl,
  And he called for his Sergeants three.
Now every Sergeant had a loud voice
  And a very loud voice had he,
"Move to the right in fours," said the Sergeant
  For merry men are we,
And there's none so fair as can compare
  With the boys of the AR-R-MY.

Old King Cole was a merry old soul,
  And a merry old soul was he,
He called for his pipe, and he called for his bowl,
  And he called for his Subalterns three.
Now every Subaltern had a big grouse,
  And a very big grouse had he,
"We do all the work," said the Subaltern.
  For merry men are we,
And there's none so fair as can compare
  With the boys of the AR-R-MY.

Old King Cole was a merry old soul,
  And a merry old soul was he,
He called for his pipe, and he called for his bowl,
  And he called for his Captains three.
Now every Captain had a fine figure,
  And a very fine figure had he,
"We want three months leave," said the Captain
  For merry men are we,
And there's none so fair as can compare
  With the boys of the AR-R-MY.

Old King Cole was a merry old soul,
  And a merry old soul was he,
He called for his pipe, and he called for his bowl,
  And he called for his Majors three.
Now every Major had a big swear,
  And a very big swear had he,
"Blankety, blankety, blank," said the Major
  For merry men are we,
And there's none so fair as can compare
  With the boys of the AR-R-MY.

Old King Cole was a merry old soul,
  And a merry old soul was he,
He called for his pipe, and he called for his bowl,
  And he called for his Colonels three.
Now every Colonel had a sore head,
  And a very sore head had he,   [Colonel,
"What's the next word of command," said the
  For merry men are we,
And there's none so fair as can compare
  With the boys of the AR-R-MY.

Old King Cole was a merry old soul,
  And a merry old soul was he,
He called for his pipe, and he called for his bowl,
  And he called for his Generals three.
Now every General had two red tabs
  And two red tabs had he,
"What's the plan of campaign," said the General,
"What's the next word of command," said the Colonel,
"Blankety, blankety, blank," said the Major,
"We want three months leave," said the Captain,
"We do all the work," said the Subaltern,
"Move to the right in fours," said the Sergeant,
"Beer! Beer! Beer!" said the Private
  Very merry men are we,
For there's none so fair as can compare
  With the boys of the AR-R-MY.

OLD TOWLER

Bright chan-ti-cleer pro-claims the dawn, And
The cor-dial takes its mer-ry round, The
Poor stag! the dogs thy haun-ches gore, The

span-gles deck the thorn;— The low-ing herds now quit the lawn, The lark springs from the corn.— Dogs,
laugh and joke pre-vail,— The hunts-man blows a jo-vial sound, The dogs snuff up— the gale;— The
tears run down thy face;— The hunts-man's plea-sure is no more, His joys were in— the chase.— A-

hunts-men, round the win-dow throng, Fleet Towl-er leads the cry,— A-rise the bur-den of— their song, "This
up-land winds they sweep a-long, O'er fields, thro' brakes they fly;— The game is rous'd, too true— the song, "This
-like the sports-men of the town, The vir-gin game in view,— Are full con-tent to run— them down, Then

day a stag must die."
day a stag must die."
they in turn pur-sue.

CHORUS

With a hey, ho, chiv-ey!— Hark for-'ard, hark for-'ard Tan-tiv-y! With a

hey, ho, chiv-ey!— Hark for-'ard hark for-'ard Tan-tiv-y! Hark for-'ard, Hark

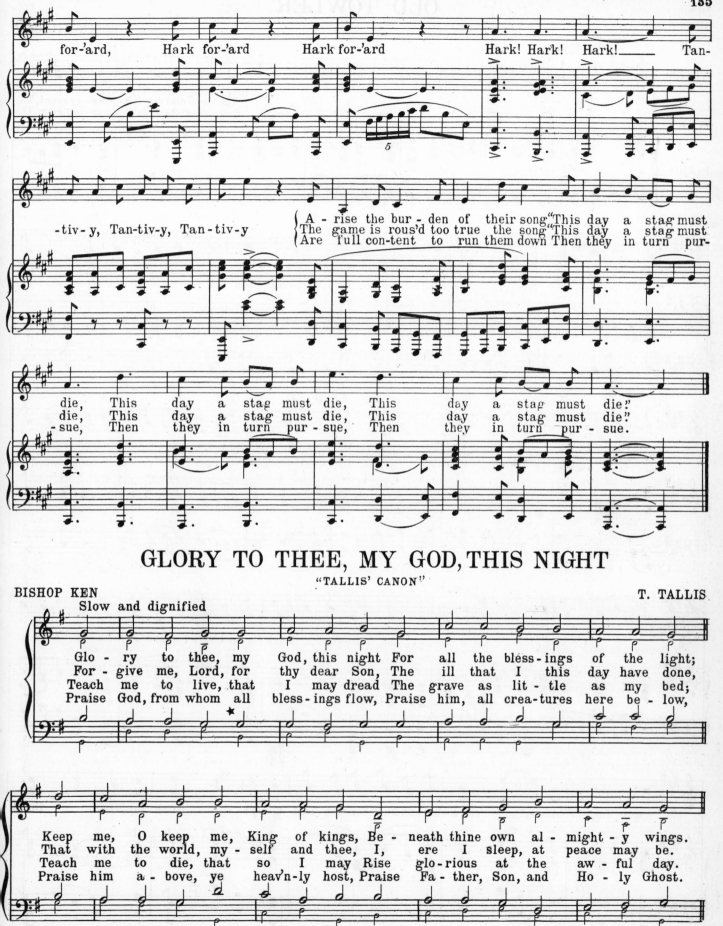

for-'ard, Hark for-'ard Hark for-'ard Hark! Hark! Hark!____ Tan-

-tiv-y, Tan-tiv-y, Tan-tiv-y

A - rise the bur - den of their song"This day a stag must
The game is rous'd too true the song"This day a stag must
Are full con-tent to run them down Then they in turn pur-

die, This day a stag must die, This day a stag must die,"
die, This day a stag must die, This day a stag must die."
-sue, Then they in turn pur - sue, Then they in turn pur - sue.

GLORY TO THEE, MY GOD, THIS NIGHT

"TALLIS' CANON"

BISHOP KEN

T. TALLIS

Slow and dignified

Glo - ry to thee, my God, this night For all the bless-ings of the light;
For - give me, Lord, for thy dear Son, The ill that I this day have done,
Teach me to live, that I may dread The grave as lit - tle as my bed;
Praise God, from whom all bless-ings flow, Praise him, all crea-tures here be - low,

Keep me, O keep me, King of kings, Be - neath thine own al - might - y wings.
That with the world, my - self and thee, I, ere I sleep, at peace may be.
Teach me to die, that so I may Rise glo - rious at the aw - ful day.
Praise him a - bove, ye heav'n-ly host, Praise Fa - ther, Son, and Ho - ly Ghost.

*When sung as a canon the second voice begins here
From "The English Hymnal"

ONE MAN WENT TO MOW

Arr. KATHLEEN MARKWELL

ONE MORE RIVER

Arr. KATHLEEN MARKWELL

SOLO 5. The animals went in three by three
CHORUS   There's one more river to cross;
SOLO   The bear, the flea, and the bumble bee.
CHORUS   There's one more river to cross, etc.

SOLO 6. The animals went in four by four,
CHORUS   There's one more river to cross;
SOLO   Old Noah got mad and hollered for more.
CHORUS   There's one more river to cross, etc.

SOLO 7. The animals went in five by five,
CHORUS   There's one more river to cross;
SOLO   With Saratoga trunks they did arrive.
CHORUS   There's one more river to cross, etc.

SOLO 8. The animals went in six by six,
CHORUS   There's one more river to cross;
SOLO   The hyena laughed at the monkey's tricks.
CHORUS   There's one more river to cross, etc.

SOLO 9. The animals went in seven by seven,
CHORUS   There's one more river to cross;
SOLO   Said the ant to the elephant, "who are you a-shovin'?"
CHORUS   There's one more river to cross, etc.

SOLO 10. The animals went in eight by eight
CHORUS   There's one more river to cross;
SOLO   They came with a rush 'cause 'twas so late.
CHORUS   There's one more river to cross, etc.

SOLO 11. The animals went in nine by nine
CHORUS   There's one more river to cross;
SOLO   Old Noah shouted, "cut that line."
CHORUS   There's one more river to cross, etc.

SOLO 12. The animals went in ten by ten,
CHORUS   There's one more river to cross;
SOLO   The ark she blew her whistle then.
CHORUS   There's one more river to cross, etc.

SOLO 13. And then the voyage did begin,
CHORUS There's one more river to cross;
SOLO Old Noah pulled the gang-plank in.
CHORUS There's one more river to cross.etc.

SOLO 14. They never knew where they were at
CHORUS There's one more river to cross;
SOLO Till the old ark bumped on Ararat.
CHORUS There's one more river to cross.etc.

SOLO 15. The old ark landed high and dry,
CHORUS There's one more river to cross;
SOLO The cow kissed the baboon good-bye.
CHORUS There's one more river to cross.etc.

SOLO 16. Now please just look out for the text,
CHORUS There's one more river to cross;
SOLO To be continued in our next.
CHORUS There's one more river to cross.etc.

GREEN GROW THE RUSHES-HO

ON ILKLEY MOOR BAHT 'AT

Arr. KATHLEEN MARKWELL

2 Tha's been a coortin' Mary Jane.

3 Tha'll go and get thi deeath o' cowld.

4 Then we shall ha' to bury thee.

5 Then t'worms'll come an' ate thee up.

6 Then t'ducks'll come an' ate up t'worms.

7 Then we shall go an' ate up t'ducks.

8 Then we shall all 'ave etten thee.

9 That's wheear we get our oahn back.

OULD JOHN BRADDLEUM

Arr. GERRARD WILLIAMS

Num - ber One,   Num - ber One;   Now my song has__ just be - gun,__
Num - ber Two,   Num - ber Two;   Some boots pinch, so__ gie I a shoe,__
Num - ber Three,   Num - ber Three;   Some likes cof - fee, and some likes tea,__
Num - ber Fowre,   Num - ber Fowre;   Some says nowt, but__ thinks the__ mowre;

} Wi' a

Rum - tum - tad - dle - um,   Ould John Brad - dle - um,   Hey, what coun - try folk we be!

5
SOLO Number Foive, Number Foive;
     Ould folks die when they can't stop alive;
CHORUS Wi' a Rum-tum-taddle-um, etc.

6
SOLO Number Six, Number Six;
     Some use crutches when they can't use sticks;
CHORUS Wi' a Rum-tum-taddle-um, etc.

7
SOLO Number Seven, Number Seven;
     Some loikes t'other place, gie I Heaven;
CHORUS Wi' a Rum-tum-taddle-um, etc.

8
SOLO Number Eight, Number Eight;
     Some folks drink till they can't walk straight;
CHORUS Wi' a Rum-tum-taddle-um, etc.

9
SOLO Number Nine, Number Nine;
     Some drinks beer 'cos they can't get wine;
CHORUS Wi' a Rum-tum-taddle-um, etc.

10
SOLO Number Ten, Number Ten;
     There beant no women where they beant no men;
CHORUS Wi' a Rum-tum-taddle-um, etc.

11
SOLO Number Eleven, Number Eleven;
     Much about t'same as number seven;
CHORUS Wi' a Rum-tum-taddle-um, etc.

12
SOLO Number Twelve, Number Twelve;
     If you wants any mowre you can sing it yerselves;
CHORUS Wi' a Rum-tum-taddle-um, etc.

O, WHO WILL O'ER THE DOWNS

Arr. KATHLEEN MARKWELL

With strength, but expressive

O, who will o'er the downs so free, O who will with me ride, O
saw her bower at twi - light grey,'Twas guard - ed safe and sure, O I
prom-ised her to come at night With com-rades brave and true, A

who will up and fol - low me, To win a bloom-ing bride? Her fath - er he has
saw her bower at break of day, 'Twas guard - ed then no more. The var - lets they were
gal - lant band with sword in hand, To break her pris - on through. I prom - ised her to

All except last time

locked the door, Her moth - er keeps the key, But neith - er door nor bolt shall part My
all a - sleep, And none was there to see The greet - ing fair that pass - ed there Be -
come at night, She's wait - ing now for me, And

Last time

own true love from me. 2 I
-tween my love and me. 3 I ere the dawn of morn - ing light I'll set my true love

free, And ere the dawn of morn - ing light I'll set my true love free.

rall.

O WILLIE BREWED A PECK O' MAUT

Arr. GERRARD WILLIAMS

With spirit

SOLO

O, — Wil - lie brewed a — peck o' maut, And — Bob and Al - len cam' to pree, Three
Here are we met, three mer - ry boys, Three mer - ry boys I trow we be; And

blith - er hearts that — lee - lang night Ye — wad - na find in Christ - en - die.
mony a nicht we've mer - ry been, And — mo - ny mair we hope to be.

CHORUS

We are na fou', we're no — that fou', But just a drap-pie in our e'e, The

End of 1st Verse *End of 2nd Verse*

cock may craw, The day may daw, But aye we'll taste the bar-ley bree. bar-ley bree.

PEACEFUL NIGHT, HOLY NIGHT

Arr. RALPH GREAVES

Peace-ful night, ho - ly night! All a - round is calm de-light;
Peace-ful night, ho - ly night! Far a - bove — a star shines bright;

See the Maid and Mo - ther mild, Watch-ing o'er — her dar - ling child,
Tell - ing all — who vi - gil keep, Pa - tient shepherds who guard their sheep,

Where he lies — a - sleep, —— Where he lies a - sleep. ——
Christ our Lord — is here, —— Christ our Lord is here. ——

THE PIPER O' DUNDEE

Arr. GERRARD WILLIAMS

POLLY - WOLLY - DOODLE

Arr. KATHLEEN MARKWELL

THE RED RIVER VALLEY

Arr. KATHLEEN MARKWELL

RICHARD OF TAUNTON DENE

Arr. GERRARD WILLIAMS

Fairly quickly and with point

SOLO

Last New Year's Day, as I've heard say, Young Rich-ard he mounted his dap - ple grey, And
Miss Jean she came with - out de - lay To hear what young Dicky had got to say; "I
"I'm hon - est, though I be but poor, I nev - er was in love be - fore; My
"Sup-pose that I should be your bride, Pray how would you for me pro - vide? For

CHORUS

trot-ted a - long from Taun - ton Dene To court the par - son's daugh - ter Jean,
s'pose you do know me, Mis - tress Jean, I'm hon - est Richard of Taun - ton Dene"
moth - er bade me come to woo, And I can fan - cy none but you." } Singing
I can neith - er sew nor spin; Pray what would your day's work bring in?"

dum-ble-dum dear - y, dum-ble-dum dear - y, dum-ble-dum dear - y, dum-ble-dum day.

5
SOLO "Why, I can plough and I can sow,
    And sometimes to market go
    With Farmer Johnson's strour and hay,
    And I can earn my ninepence every day.
      CHORUS Singing etc.

6
SOLO "Ninepence a day will never do,
    For I must have silks and satins too;
    Ninepence a day won't buy us meat!'
    "Adzooks", says Dick, "I've a sack of wheat."
      CHORUS Singing etc.

7
SOLO Dick's compliments did so delight,
    They made the family laugh outright.
    Young Richard took huff, no more would say;
    He kicked up old Dobbin and rode away.
      CHORUS Singing etc.

THE RIO GRANDE

Arr. ARCHIBALD JACOB

With a swing

PIANO

mf

mf SOLO

O say, were you ev - er in Ri - o Grande,
bye, fare you well, all you la - dies of town,
pack up your don - key and get un - der way,
you Bower-y la - dies, we'd have you to know,

f CHORUS

O_____ Ri - o_____

mf SOLO

It's
We've
The
We're

there that the ri - ver runs down gold-en strand, And we're bound for the Ri - o Grande.
left you e - nough for to buy a silk gown. For we're bound for the Ri - o Grande.
girls we are leav-ing can take our half-pay For we're bound for the Ri - o Grande.
bound to the Southward, O Lord let us go! For we're bound for the Ri - o Grande.

ff CHORUS

Then a - way love, a - way, Way_____ down Ri - o_____ O,

All except last Chor. | *Last time*

fare ye well, my pret-ty young gel, For we're bound for the Ri - o Grande. And good Grande
So it's
Now

ROBIN ADAIR

Arr. ARCHIBALD JACOB

What's this dull town to me? Ro-bin's not here.
What made th'as-sem-bly shine? Ro-bin A-dair.
But now thou'rt cold to me, Ro-bin A-dair.

What was't I wished to see? What wished to hear?
What made the ball so fine? Ro-bin A-dair.
And I no more shall see Ro-bin A-dair.

Where's all the joy and mirth Made this_ town a heav'n on earth?
What when the play was o'er, What made my heart so sore?
Yet him I loved so well Still in_ my heart shall dwell;

Oh! they're all_ fled with thee, Ro-bin_ A-dair.
Oh! it_ was_ part-ing with Ro-bin_ A-dair.
Oh! I_ can_ ne'er for-get Ro-bin_ A-dair.

ROW, DOW, DOW, OR THE DRUM

Arr. GERRARD WILLIAMS

*A SAFE STRONGHOLD OUR GOD IS STILL

"EIN' FESTE BURG"

Tr. THOMAS CARLYLE

MARTIN LUTHER

Very slow and solemn

A safe strong-hold our God is still,
With force of arms we noth-ing can,
And God's word, for all their craft and

A trus-ty shield and wea - pon;
Full soon were we down - rid - den;
And watch-ing to de - vour us,

He'll help us clear from all the ill
But for us fights the prop-er Man,
We lay it not to heart so sore;

That hath us now o'er - tak - en.
Whom God him-self hath bid - den.
Not they can ov - er - power us.

The an-cient prince of hell
Ask ye, Who is this same?
And let the prince of ill

Hath ris'n with pur-pose fell;
Christ Je - sus is His name,
Look grim as e'er he will,

And though they take our life,
Goods, hon-our, child - ren, wife,

Strong mail of craft and pow'r He wear - eth in this
The Lord Sa - ba - oth's Son; He, and no oth - er
He harms us not a whit; For why?— his doom is
Yet is their prof - it small; These things shall van - ish

hour; On earth is not his fel - low.
one, Shall con-quer in the bat - tle.
writ; A word shall quick - ly slay him.
all, The cit - y of God re - main - eth.

*From "The English Hymnal"

THE SAILOR LIKES HIS BOTTLE, O

Arr. GERRARD WILLIAMS

ST. PATRICK WAS A GENTLEMAN

Arr. ARCHIBALD JACOB

Quick, and with humour

f SOLO

VOICE

Oh, St. Pat-rick was a gen-tle-man, Who came of de-cent
The Wick-low hills are ver-y high, And so's the Hill of
There's not a mile in Ireland's isle Where dir-ty varmint
Nine hundred thousand rep-tiles blue He charm'd with sweet dis-

PIANO

f

peo - ple; He built a church in Dub - lin town, And on it put a stee - ple. His fath - er was a
Howth, sir; But there's a hill much big - ger still, Much high-er nor them both, sir. 'Twas on the top of
mus - ters, But there he put his dear fore-foot, And mur-der'd them in clus-ters. The toads went pop the
cours - es, And dined on them at Kil - la - loe In soups and sec - ond cours-es. Where blind-worms crawling

Gall - ag - her, His moth - er was a Bra - dy; His aunt was an O' Shaughnes - sy His un - cle was an O' Gra-dy.
this high hill St. Pat-rick preach'd his sarmint, That drove the frogs in - to the bogs, And ban-ish'd all the varmint.
frogs went hop, Slap - dash in - to the wat - er, And the snakes committed su - i - cide To save themselves from slaughter.
in the grass Dis - gust - ed all the na-tion, He gave them a rise which open'd their eyes To a sense of their si - tu - a - tion.

ff CHORUS

So suc - cess at-tend St. Pat-rick's fist, For he's a Saint so clev - er; Oh he

ff

gave the snakes and toads a twist, And ban - ished them for ev - er.

SALLY BROWN

Arr. RALPH GREAVES

SOLO   Sally Brown, I'm bound to leave you,
CHORUS Way-ay-a, Roll and go.
SOLO   Sally Brown, I'll not deceive you.
CHORUS Spend my money on Sally Brown.

5

SOLO   Sally lives on the old plantation,
CHORUS Way-ay-a, Roll and go.
SOLO   She belongs to Wild Goose nation.
CHORUS Spend my money on Sally Brown.

SALLY IN OUR ALLEY

Arr. KATHLEEN MARKWELL

SCOTS WHA HAE

Arr. KATHLEEN MARKWELL

THE SHAN VAN VOCHT

Arr. RALPH GREAVE

SHENANDOAH

Arr. RALPH GREAVES

SHULE AGRA

A. P. GRAVES

Arr. KATHLEEN MARKWELL

Lyrics (verses):

His hair was black, his eye was blue, His arm was stout, his word was true. I wish in my heart I was with you. Go thee thu Ma-vour-neen slaun.

sold my rock, I sold my reel, When my flax was spun, I sold my wheel, To buy my love a sword of steel. Go thee thu Ma-vour-neen slaun.

dye my petticoat, I'll dye it red, And round the world I'll beg my bread, Till I find my love, a-live or dead Go thee thu Ma-vour-neen slaun.

CHORUS: Shule, Shule, shule a-gra! Only death can ease my woe, Since the lad of my heart from me did go, Go thee thu Ma-vour-neen slaun!

★ Farewell, my darling
† Come, come, my love

Fine

SIR EGLAMORE

Arr. KATHEEN MARKWELL

SOLO   When all was done to the ale-house he went,
CHORUS   Fa, la, lanky down dilly,
SOLO   And presently his tuppence was spent,
CHORUS   Fa, la, lanky down dilly,
SOLO   He was so hot with fighting the dragon,
And nought could quench his thirst but a flagon.
CHORUS   Fa, la, la, la, Fa la lanky down dilly.

SOLO   Well now let us pray for the King and the Queen,
CHORUS   Fa, la, lanky down dilly,
SOLO   And eke in London that may be seen,
CHORUS   Fa, la, lanky down dilly,
SOLO   As many knights and as many more,
And all as good as Sir Eglamore:
CHORUS   Fa, la, la, la, Fa la lanky down dilly.

SO EARLY IN DE MORNING

Arr. KATHLEEN MARKWELL

SOLO

South Car - o - lina's a sul - try clime, We used to work in the Sum - mer - time;
When I was young I used to wait, On mas - sa's tab - le lay de plate;
Now mas - sa's dead an' gone to rest, Of all the mas - sa's he was best;

Mas sa 'neath de shade would lay, While we poor nig - gers toiled all day.
Pass de bot - tle when him dry, Brush a - way de blue - tailed fly.
I nebber see de like since I was born, Miss him now he's dead and gone.

CHORUS

So_ ear - ly in de morn-ing, So_ ear-ly in de morn-ing, So_ ear-ly in de

morn-ing, Be - fore de break of day.

SONG OF THE WESTERN MEN

Arr. RALPH GREAVES

SONG OF THE VOLGA BOATMEN

The melody to be hummed or vocalised on "oo" or "ah"

Arr. KATHLEEN MARKWELL

✻ YE WATCHERS AND YE HOLY ONES
"LASST UNS ERFREUEN"

A.R.

In moderate time, dignified

Ye watchers and ye ho-ly ones, Bright Seraphs, Cherubim and Thrones, Raise the glad strain, Al-le-
O higher than the Cherubim, More glorious than the Seraphim, Lead their prais-es, Al-le-
Re-spond, ye souls in endless rest, Ye Patriarchs and Prophets blest, Al-le-lu - ia, Al-le-
O friends, in gladness let us sing, Su-per-nal anthems echo - ing, Al-le-lu - ia, Al-le-

-lu - ia! Cry out Do-minions, Princedoms, Pow'rs', Vir - tues, Arch-an-gels, An-gels' choirs,
-lu - ia! Thou Bear-er of the e-ter-nal Word, Most gracious, mag-ni - fy the Lord,
-lu - ia! Ye ho - ly Twelve, ye Martyrs strong, All Saints tri-um-phant, raise the song
-lu - ia! To God the Fa-ther, God the Son, And God the Spi - rit, Three in One,

Al-le-lu - ia, Al-le-lu - ia, Al-le-lu - ia, Al-le-lu - ia, Al-le-lu - ia!

SPANISH LADIES

Arr. KATHLEEN MARKWELL

STORMALONG

Arr. S. TAYLOR HARRIS

Slowly and with great longing

SOLO

VOICE

PIANO

mp with weight

O

poor   old Storm — y's   dead   and   gone
Storm — y's dead,   I   saw   him   die
dug   his grave   with a   sil — ver   spade
lowered   him down   with a   gold — en   chain
now   we'll sing   his fun — er — al   song

CHORUS

To me way   storm — a —

SOLO

O   poor   old Storm — y's   dead   and   gone
Old   Storm — y's dead,   I   saw   him   die
We   dug   his grave   with a   sil — ver   spade
We   lowered   him down   with a   gold — en   chain
And   now   we'll sing   his fun — er — al   song

-long

CHORUS

All except last chorus   *Last time*

Aye   aye   aye   Mis — ter   Storm — a — long

2. Old
3. We
4. We
5. And

Storm — a — long

STRAWBERRY FAIR

Arr. KATHLEEN MARKWELL

SWING LOW, SWEET CHARIOT

Arr. RALPH GREAVES

THERE IS A TAVERN IN THE TOWN

Arr. ARCHIBALD JACOB

There is a tav-ern in the
He left me for a dam-sel
Oh! dig my grave both wide and

town, in the town, And there my dear love sits him down, sits him down, And
dark, dam-sel dark, Each Fri - day night they used to spark, used to spark, And
deep, wide and deep, Put tomb - stones at my head and feet, head and feet, And

drinks his wine 'mid laugh-ter free And nev - er, nev-er, thinks of me.
now my love, once true to me, Takes that dark damsel on his knee.
on my breast carve a tur - tle dove, To sig - ni - fy I died of love.

Fare thee well, for I must leave thee, Do not let the part-ing grieve thee, And re-

mem-ber that the best of friends must part, must part, A - dieu, kind friends, a-dieu, a-

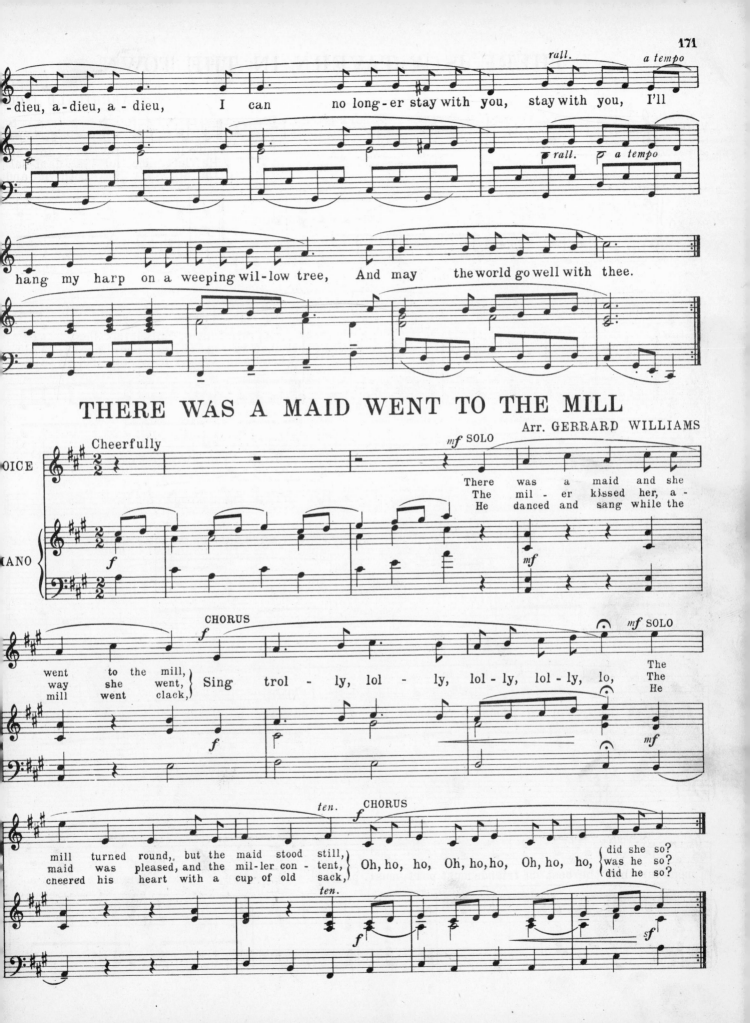

-dieu, a-dieu, a-dieu, I can no long-er stay with you, stay with you, I'll

hang my harp on a weeping wil-low tree, And may the world go well with thee.

THERE WAS A MAID WENT TO THE MILL

Arr. GERRARD WILLIAMS

There was a maid and she
The mil-er kissed her, a-
He danced and sang while the

went to the mill,
way she went, } Sing trol-ly, lol-ly, lol-ly, lol-ly, lo, The
mill she went clack, The
He

mill turned round, but the maid stood still,
maid was pleased, and the mil-ler con-tent, } Oh, ho, ho, Oh, ho, ho, Oh, ho, ho, { did she so?
cheered his heart with a cup of old sack, was he so?
did he so?

THE TAILOR AND THE MOUSE

Arr. KATHLEEN MARKWELL

THE THREE CROWS

Arr. RALPH GREAVES

THREE FISHERS

(JOHN HULLAH)

CHARLES KINGSLEY

THE THREE RAVENS

Arr. KATHLEEN MARKWELL

TOM'S GONE TO HILO

Arr. RALPH GREAVES

TURN YE TO ME

JOHN WILSON

Arr. ARCHIBALD JACOB

The stars are shin - ing cheer - i - ly, cheer - i - ly, Ho - ro, Mhairi dhu, Turn ye to me, The
The waves are danc - ing mer - ri - ly, mer - ri - ly, Ho - ro, Mhairi dhu, Turn ye to me, The

sea-mew is moan - ing drear - i - ly, drear - i - ly, Ho - ro, Mhai-ridhu, Turn ye to me.
sea-birds are wail - ing wear - i - ly, wear - i - ly, Ho - ro, Mhai-ridhu, Turn ye to me.

Cold is the storm-wind that ruf-fles his breast, But warm are the down-y plumes lin-ing his nest,
Hushed be thy moan-ing, lone bird of the sea, Thy home on the rock is a shel-ter to thee; Thy

Cold blows the storm there, soft falls the snow there, Ho - ro, Mhairi dhu, Turn ye to me.
home is the an-gry wave, mine but the lone-ly grave, Ho - ro, Mhairi dhu, Turn ye to me.

TWANKYDILLO

Arr. ARCHIBALD JACOBS

With good rhythm

VOICE

f SOLO

Here's health to the jol-ly black-smith, the
If a gen-tle-man calls his
Here's a health to King Char-lie and

PIANO

best of all fel-lows, Who works at his an-vil while the boy blows the bel-lows; Which
horse for to shoe, He makes no de-ni-al of _ one pot or two, For it
al-so his queen, And to all the royal lit-tle ones where _ e'er they are seen, Which

makes my bright ham-mer to rise and to fall, Here's to old Cole, and to young Cole, and to

rall. old Cole of all.

ff **CHORUS** *a tempo*

Twan-ky-dil - lo, Twan-ky-dil - lo, Twan-ky-dil - lo, dil - lo, dil - lo,
Twan-ky-dil - lo, Twan-ky-dil - lo, Twan-ky-dil - lo, dil - lo, dil - lo,
Twan-ky-dil - lo, Twan-ky-dil - lo, Twan-ky-dil - lo, dil - lo, dil - lo,

dil - lo, A roar-ing pair of bag-pipes made of the green wil-low.
dil - lo, And he that loves strong beer is a heart-y good fel-low.
dil - lo, A roar-ing pair of bag-pipes made of the green wil-low

UPIDEE

From LONGFELLOW

Arr. KATHLEEN MARKWELL

VESPER HYMN

MOORE

Arr. GERRARD WILLIAMS

VIVE L'AMOUR

Arr. ERIC MAREO

SOLO	Come, fill up your glasses: I'll give you a toast,	SOLO	Since all with good humour you've toasted with me,
CHORUS	Vive la compagnie!	CHORUS	Vive la compagnie!
SOLO	Here's a health to our friend, our kind worthy host,	SOLO	I hope it will please you to drink now with me,
CHORUS	Vive la compagnie!	CHORUS	Vive la compagnie!
CHORUS	Vive la, etc.	CHORUS	Vive la, etc.

THE VICAR OF BRAY

In march time, with humour

Arr. ARCHIBALD JACOB

SOLO

In good King Charles's gold-en days, When loy-al-ty no harm meant, A zeal-ous High-Church-
When Roy-al James pos-sess'd the crown, And Pope-ry came in fash-ion, The pen-al laws I
When Wil-liam was our King de-clar'd, To ease the na-tion's griev-ance,With this new wind a-
When roy-al Ann be-came our Queen,The Church of Eng-land's glo-ry, An o-ther face of

man was I, And so I got pre-fer-ment, To teach my flock I nev-er miss'd, Kings
hoot-ed down, And read the De-clar-a-tion;The Church of Rome I found would fit, Full
bout I steer'd, And swore to him al-le-giance,Old prin-ci-ples I did re-voke, Set
things was seen, And I be-came a To-ry; Oc-cas-ion-al con-form-ists base, I

were by God ap-point-ed, And lost are those that dare re-sist, Or touch the Lord's a-noint-ed.
well my con-sti-tu-tion;And I had been a Jes-u-it, But for the Re-vol-u-tion.
cons-cience at a dis-tance;Pas-sive o-bed-iance was a joke, A jest was non-re-sist-ance.
blam'd their mod-er-a-tion;And though the Church in dan-ger was, By such pre-var-i-ca-tion.

CHORUS

And this is law I will maintain, Un-til my dy-ing day, Sir, That

When George in pudding-time came o'er,
  And moderate men looked big, Sir,
My principles I changed once more,
  And so became a Whig, Sir,
And thus preferment I procured
  From our new faith's-defender;
And almost every day abjured
  The Pope and the Pretender.

CHORUS And this is law, &c.

Th' illustrious house of Hanover,
  And Protestant succession,
To them I do allegiance swear—
  While they can hold possession
For in my faith and loyalty
  I never more will falter,
And George my lawful King shall be—
  Until the times do alter.

CHORUS And this is law, &c.

★ HE WHO WOULD VALIANT BE

"MONKS GATE"

J. BUNYAN, and others

TRADITIONAL MELODY

*From "The English Hymnal": By permission of the Oxford University Press

WE BE THREE POOR MARINERS

Arr. GERRARD WILLIAMS

We be three poor ma-ri-ners New-ly come from the seas, We spend our lives in
We care not for those mar-tial men That do our states dis-dain, But we care for the

jeo-par-dy—While oth-ers live at ease. Come let us dance the
mer-chant-men—Who do our states main-tain. To them we dance this

round a-round a-round, Come let us dance the round a-round a-round, And
round a-round a-round, To them we dance this round a-round a-round, And

he that is a bul-ly boy,—Come pledge me on the ground a-ground a-ground.

WE'RE ALL BOUND TO GO

Arr. S. TAYLOR HARRIS

I was strol - ling out one day, Down by the Al - bert Dock,
- morn - ing Mis - ter Taps - cott, sir" "Good morn - ing me gal" says he,
he "My dear, now have no fear But come a - long with me,

Heave a -way my John - ny, Heave a - way a - way "O For

saw a charm - ing I - rish gal, A talk - ing to Taps - cott,
have you got a pack - et ship, A - bound for A - mer - i - kee,"
I have got a pack - et ship, To car - ry you o - ver the sea"

Heave a -

- way my John - ny boys, We're all bound to go. 2 "Good
3 Said

THE WEST'S AWAKE

Arr. GERRARD WILLIAMS

Fairly slow and with strength.

When
That

all be-side a vig-il keep, The West's a-sleep, the West's a-sleep. A-
chain-less wave and love-ly land Freedom and Na-tion-hood de-mand. Be

-las, and well may E-rin weep That Con-nacht lies in slum-ber deep. There
sure the great God nev-er planned That For slum-b'ring slaves a home so grand. And

lake and plain smile fair and free, 'Mid rocks their guardian chiv-al-ry, Sing
long a proud and haugh-ty race Honoured and sen-ti-nelled the place. Sing

oh! let man learn lib-er-ty From crash-ing wind and lash-ing sea!
oh! not e'en their sons' dis-grace Can quite des-troy their glo-ry's trace.

WHAT SHALL WE DO WITH THE DRUNKEN SAILOR?

Arr. RALPH GREAVES

WHISKY JOHNNY

Arr. RALPH GREAVES

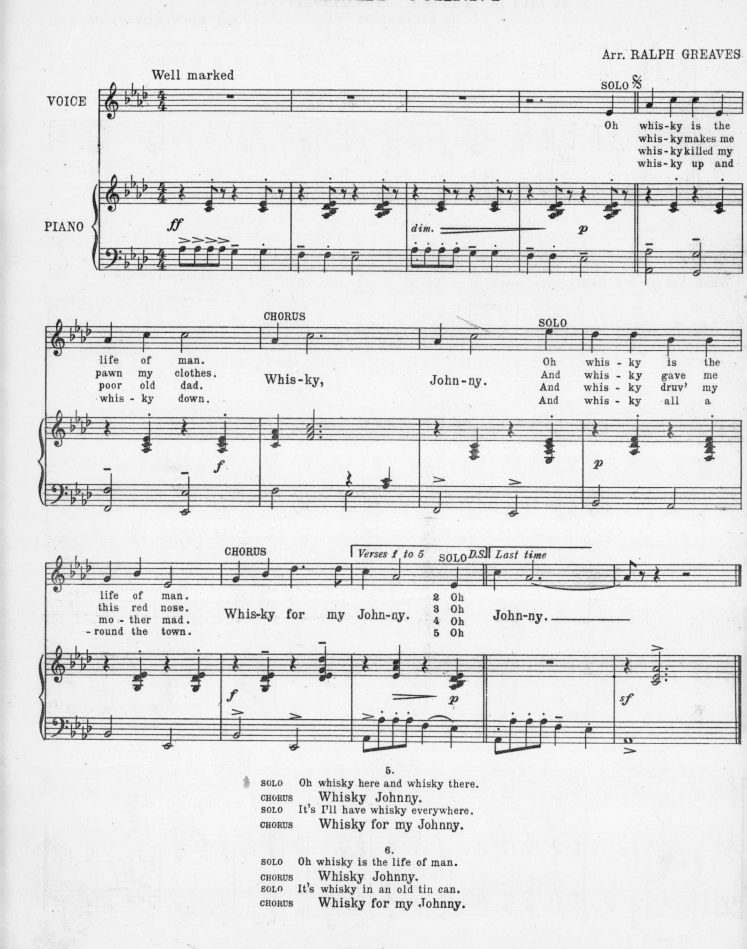

5.

SOLO   Oh whisky here and whisky there.
CHORUS   **Whisky Johnny.**
SOLO   It's I'll have whisky everywhere.
CHORUS   **Whisky for my Johnny.**

6.

SOLO   Oh whisky is the life of man.
CHORUS   **Whisky Johnny.**
SOLO   It's whisky in an old tin can.
CHORUS   **Whisky for my Johnny.**

WHO'S THAT A-CALLING

(J. B. LAWREER)

Arr. KATHLEEN MARKWELL

WI' A HUNDRED PIPERS AN' A'

LADY NAIRNE

Arr. ARCHIBALD JACOB

WIDDICOMBE FAIR

Arr. ARCHIBALD JACOB

5

SOLO So Tom Pearce's old mare her took sick and died,
CHORUS All along, down along, out along lee.
SOLO And Tom he sat down on a stone and he cried
With Bill Brewer, Jan Stewer, Peter Gurney,
Peter Davy, Dan'l Whiddon, Harry Hawke,
CHORUS Old Uncle Tom Cobleigh and all—
Old Uncle Tom Cobleigh and all.

7

SOLO When the wind whistles cold on the moor of a night
CHORUS All along, down along, out along lee.
SOLO Tom Pearce's old mare doth appear ghastly white
With Bill Brewer, Jan Stewer, Peter Gurney,
Peter Davy, Dan'l Whiddon, Harry Hawke,
CHORUS Old Uncle Tom Cobleigh and all— etc.

6

SOLO But this isn't the end o' this shocking affair,
CHORUS All along, down along, out along lee.
SOLO Nor, tho' they be dead, of the horrid career
Of Bill Brewer, Jan Stewer, Peter Gurney,
Peter Davy, Dan'l Whiddon, Harry Hawke,
CHORUS Old Uncle Tom Cobleigh and all.—
Old Uncle Tom Cobleigh and all.

8

SOLO And all the night long he heard skirling and groans
CHORUS All along, down along, out along lee.
SOLO From Tom Pearce's old mare in her rattling bones
With Bill Brewer, Jan Stewer, Peter Gurney,
Peter Davy, Dan'l Whiddon, Harry Hawke,
CHORUS Old Uncle Tom Cobleigh and all— etc.

THE WRAGGLE-TAGGLE GIPSIES, O!

Arr. KATHLEEN MARKWELL

With good rhythm

ALL TOGETHER

Three gip - sies stood at the
They sang so sweet, they
She pluck - ed off her

Cas - tle gate, They sang so high, they sang so low, The
sang so shrill, That fast her tears be - gan to flow. And
high - heeled shoes, A - made of Span - ish leath - er, O. She

la - dy sate in her cham - ber late, Her heart it melt - ed a - way as snow.
she laid down her silk - en gown, Her gold - en rings and all her show.
would in the street, with her bare, bare feet; All out in the wind and weath - er O.

4
MENS' VOICES

O saddle to me my milk-white steed,
  And go and fetch me my pony, O!
That I may ride and seek my bride,
  Who is gone with the wraggle-taggle gipsies, O!

5
ALL TOGETHER

O he rode high, and he rode low,
  He rode through wood and copses too,
Until he came to an open field,
  And there he espied his a-lady, O!

6
MENS' VOICES

What makes you leave your house and land?
  Your golden treasures for to go?
What makes you leave your new-wedded lord,
  To follow the wraggle taggle-gipsies, O!

7
WOMENS' VOICES

What care I for my house and my land?
  What care I for my treasure, O?
What care I for my new-wedded lord,
  I'm off with the wraggle-taggle gipsies, O!

8
MENS' VOICES

Last night you slept on a goose-feather bed,
  With the sheet turned down so bravely, O!
And to-night you'll sleep in a cold open field,
  Along with the wraggle-taggle gipsies, O!

9
WOMENS' VOICES

What care I for a goose-feather bed,
  With the sheet turned down so bravely, O!
For to-night I shall sleep in a cold open field,
  Along with the wraggle-taggle gipsies, O!

Rounds and Canons

COME FOLLOW

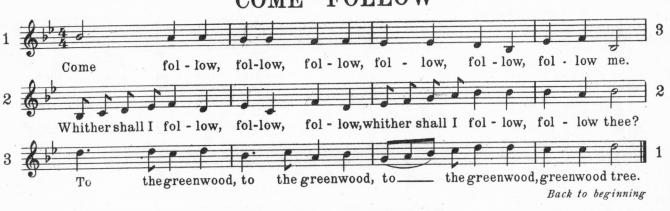

Come fol-low, fol-low, fol-low, fol-low, fol-low, fol-low me.

Whither shall I fol-low, fol-low, fol-low, whither shall I fol-low, fol-low thee?

To the greenwood, to the greenwood, to____ the greenwood, greenwood tree.

Back to beginning

GO, GO, BANISH

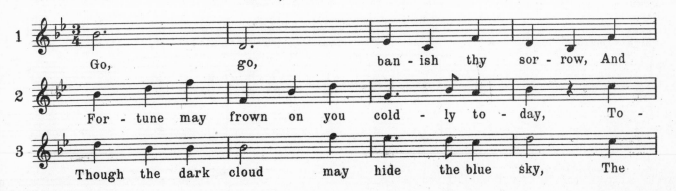

Go, go, ban-ish thy sor-row, And

For-tune may frown on you cold-ly to-day, To-

Though the dark cloud may hide the blue sky, The

think of the pre-sent no more;

-mor-row with bless-ings your lot may run o'er;

sun will be__ shin-ing by-and-by.

GO TO JOAN GLOVER

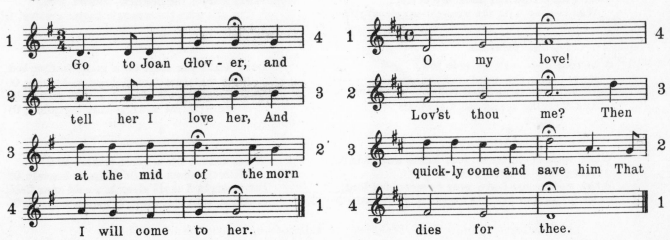

Go to Joan Glov-er, and

tell her I love her, And

at the mid of the morn

I will come to her.

O MY LOVE

O my love!

Lov'st thou me? Then

quick-ly come and save him That

dies for thee.

GREAT TOM IS CAST

HENRY LAWES

Great Tom is cast, And
Christ Church bells ring 1, 2, 3, 4, 5,
6, And Tom comes last.

HEY HO, TO THE GREENWOOD

WILLIAM BYRD

Hey, ho____ to the green - wood now let us go, sing heave_ and

Hey ho,____ to the green - wood now let us

Hey Ho,____ to the

ho, And there shall we find both buck and doe, sing heave_

go sing heave and ho And there shall we find both buck_

green - wood now let us go, sing heave and ho, And

and ho, The hart and hind and the lit-tle pret - ty roe, sing

_ and doe, sing heave and ho, The hart and hind and the

there shall we find both buck and doe, sing heave_ and ho,

heave and ho, Hey ho_____ to the greenwood now

lit-tle pret - ty roe, sing heave and ho, Hey ho____

The hart and hind, and the little pret - ty roe, sing heave and ho

LONDON'S BURNING

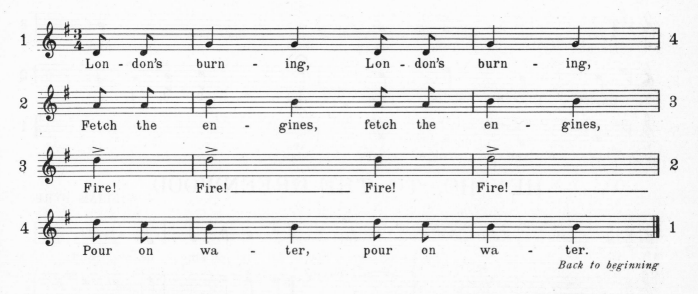

1. Lon-don's burn - ing, Lon - don's burn - ing,
2. Fetch the en - gines, fetch the en - gines,
3. Fire! Fire! Fire! Fire!
4. Pour on wa - ter, pour on wa - ter.

Back to beginning

MY DAME HATH A LAME TAME CRANE

MATTHEW WHITE

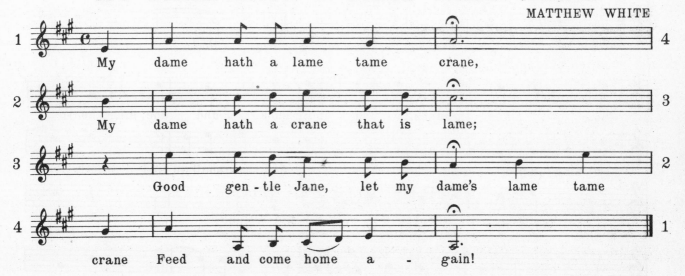

1. My dame hath a lame tame crane,
2. My dame hath a crane that is lame;
3. Good gen - tle Jane, let my dame's lame tame
4. crane Feed and come home a - gain!

NOW ROBIN LEND TO ME THY BOW

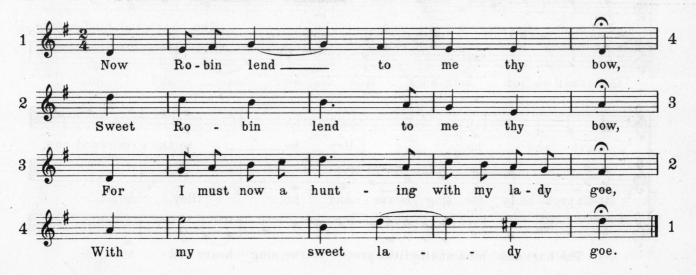

1. Now Ro - bin lend to me thy bow,
2. Sweet Ro - bin lend to me thy bow,
3. For I must now a hunt - ing with my la - dy goe,
4. With my sweet la - dy goe.

SUMER IS ICUMEN IN

Sum - er is i - cu - men in___ Lhu - de sing cuc - cu

Grow - eth sed, And blow - eth med, And sping - 'th the wd - e nu.

Sing cuc - cu, Aw - e blet - eth af - ter lomb, Lhouth

af - ter cal - ve cu, Bul - luc ster - teth, Buck - e vert - eth,

Mu - rie sing cu - cu, cu - cu, cuc - cu, Wel

sing - es thu cuc - cu. Ne___ swik thu na - ver nu; *Back to beginning*

These four bars are repeated ad infinitum by two male voices

cuc - cu, cuc - cu,___ cuc - cu, cuc - cu.___

* *The 2nd, 3rd and 4th voices enter in turn, when previous part has reached the beginning of the third bar.*

THREE BLIND MICE

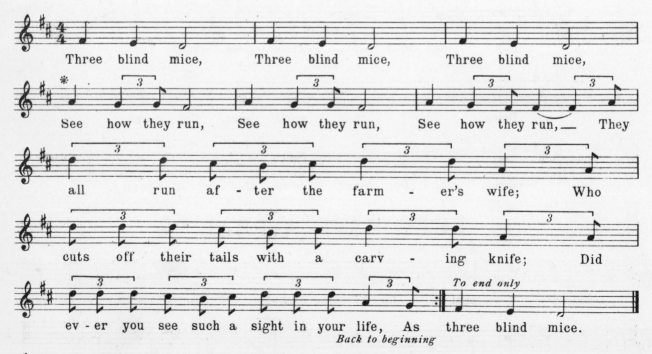

Three blind mice, Three blind mice, Three blind mice,

See how they run, See how they run, See how they run,___ They

all run af - ter the farm - er's wife; Who

cuts off their tails with a carv - ing knife; Did

ev - er you see such a sight in your life, As three blind mice.
Back to beginning

* *The 2nd and 3rd voices enter when the previous voice has reached this point.*

THE WISEMEN

WILLIAM LAWES

The Wise - men were but sev'n, _____ Ne'er more shall be for me; ___
The Vir - tues they were sev'n, _____ And three the great - er be; ___

The Mu - ses were but nine, _____ The Wor - thies three time three: __
The Cae - sars they were twelve, _____ And the Fat - al Sis - ters three: __

And three mer-ry boys, and three mer-ry boys, and three mer-ry boys, Are we. ___
And three mer-ry girls, and three mer-ry girls, and three mer-ry girls, Are we. ___

WHITE SAND AND GREY SAND

White sand and grey sand,

Who'll buy my grey sand,

Who'll buy my white sand.

UP AND DOWN

MATTHEW LOCK

Up and down this world goes round,

Down, this world goes. Up and

down, Up and down this world goes.

LET'S HAVE A PEAL

Let's have a peal for __ John Cook's soul; For he was a

ve - ry, ve - ry hon - est man, An hon - est man.

*The 2nd, 3rd, 4th, 5th, 6th, 7th, 8th and 9th voices enter when the previous voice has reached this point

For the Very Young

DILLY DILLY

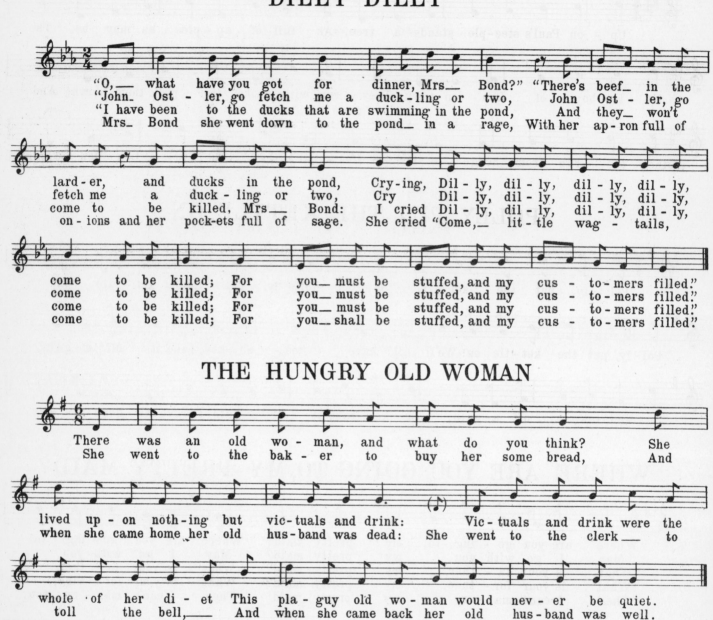

"O,__ what have you got for dinner, Mrs__ Bond?" "There's beef__ in the
"John__ Ost-ler, go fetch me a duck-ling or two, John Ost-ler, go
"I have been to the ducks that are swimming in the pond, And they__ won't
Mrs__ Bond she went down to the pond__ in a rage, With her ap-ron full of

lard-er, and ducks in the pond, Cry-ing, Dil-ly, dil-ly, dil-ly, dil-ly,
fetch me a duck-ling or two, Cry Dil-ly, dil-ly, dil-ly, dil-ly,
come to be killed, Mrs__ Bond: I cried Dil-ly, dil-ly, dil-ly, dil-ly,
on-ions and her pock-ets full of sage. She cried "Come,__ lit-tle wag-tails,

come to be killed; For you__ must be stuffed, and my cus-to-mers filled."
come to be killed; For you__ must be stuffed, and my cus-to-mers filled."
come to be killed; For you__ must be stuffed, and my cus-to-mers filled."
come to be killed; For you__ shall be stuffed, and my cus-to-mers filled."

THE HUNGRY OLD WOMAN

There was an old wo-man, and what do you think? She
She went to the bak-er to buy her some bread, And

lived up-on noth-ing but vic-tuals and drink: Vic-tuals and drink were the
when she came home her old hus-band was dead: She went to the clerk__ to

whole of her di-et This pla-guy old wo-man would nev-er be quiet.
toll the bell,__ And when she came back her old hus-band was well.

IF ALL THE WORLD WERE PAPER

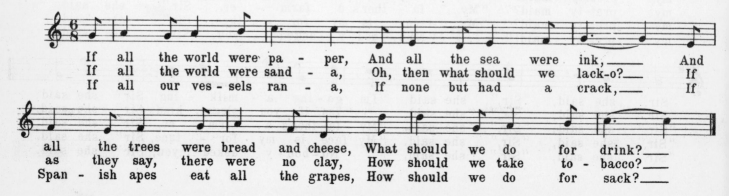

If all the world were pa-per, And all the sea were ink,__ And
If all the world were sand-a, Oh, then what should we lack-o?__ If
If all our ves-sels ran-a, If none but had a crack,__ If

all the trees were bread and cheese, What should we do for drink?__
as they say, there were no clay, How should we take to-bacco?__
Span-ish apes eat all the grapes, How should we do for sack?__

PAUL'S STEEPLE

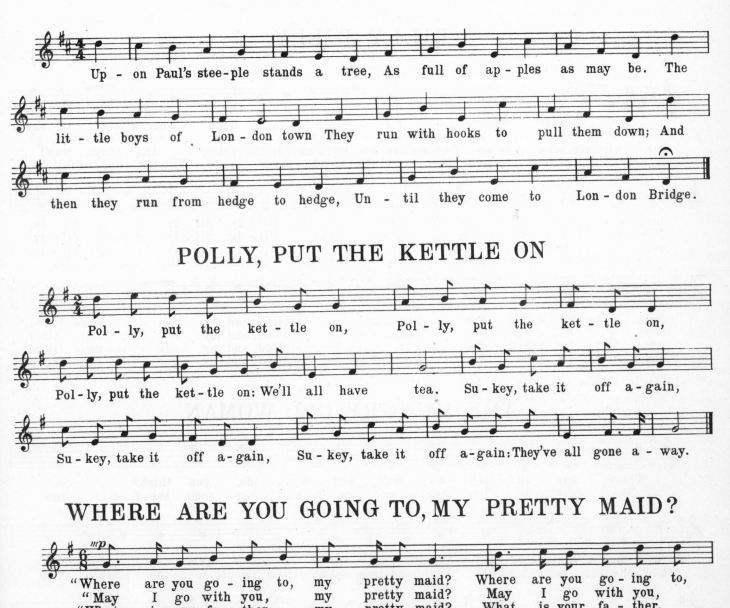

Up - on Paul's stee-ple stands a tree, As full of ap - ples as may be. The
lit - tle boys of Lon - don town They run with hooks to pull them down; And
then they run from hedge to hedge, Un - til they come to Lon - don Bridge.

POLLY, PUT THE KETTLE ON

Pol - ly, put the ket - tle on, Pol - ly, put the ket - tle on,
Pol - ly, put the ket - tle on: We'll all have tea. Su - key, take it off a - gain,
Su - key, take it off a - gain, Su - key, take it off a - gain: They've all gone a - way.

WHERE ARE YOU GOING TO, MY PRETTY MAID?

"Where are you go - ing to, my pretty maid? Where are you go - ing to,
"May I go with you, my pretty maid? May I go with you,
"What is your fa - ther, my pretty maid? What is your fa - ther,
"What is your for - tune, my pretty maid? What is your for - tune,
"Then I can't mar - ry you, my pretty maid! Then I can't mar - ry you,

my pret - ty maid?" "I'm go - ing a - milk - ing, Sir," she said,
my pret - ty maid?" "Yes, if you please, kind Sir," she said,
my pret - ty maid?" "My fa - ther's a farm - er, Sir," she said,
my pret - ty maid?" "My face is my for - tune, Sir," she said,
my pret - ty maid!" "No - bod - y asked you, Sir," she said,

"Sir," she said, "Sir," she said, "I'm go - ing a - milk - ing, Sir" she said.
"Sir," she said, "Sir," she said, "Yes, if you please, kind Sir" she said.
"Sir," she said, "Sir," she said, "My fa - ther's a farm - er, Sir" she said.
"Sir," she said, "Sir," she said, "My face is my for - tune, Sir" she said.
"Sir," she said, "Sir," she said, "No - bod - y asked you, Sir" she said.

GREEN GRAVEL

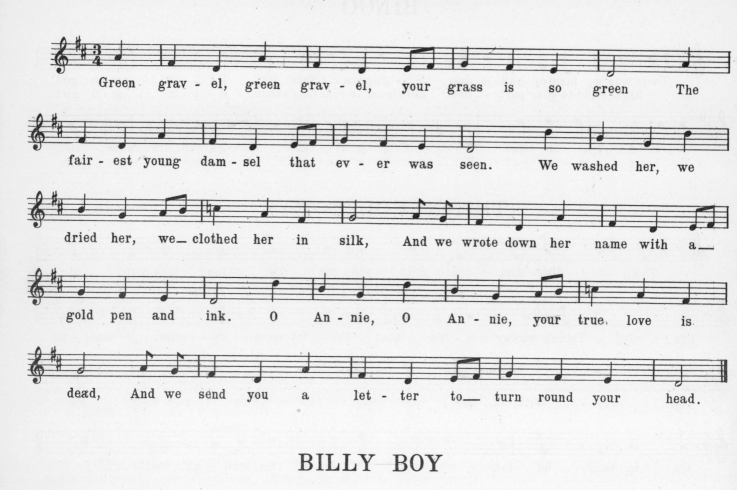

Green grav-el, green grav-el, your grass is so green The
fair-est young dam-sel that ev-er was seen. We washed her, we
dried her, we clothed her in silk, And we wrote down her name with a
gold pen and ink. O An-nie, O An-nie, your true love is
dead, And we send you a let-ter to turn round your head.

BILLY BOY

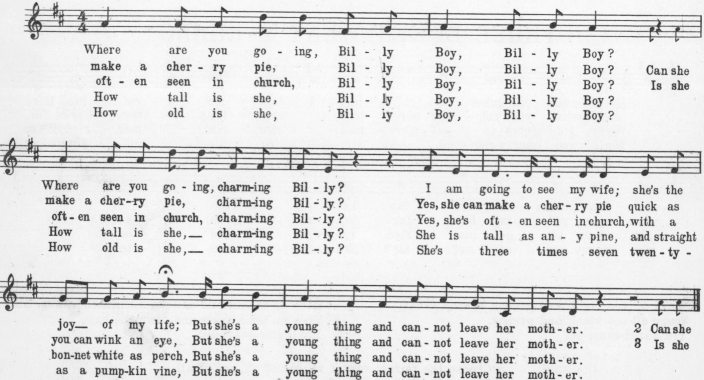

Where are you go-ing, Bil-ly Boy, Bil-ly Boy?
make a cher-ry pie, Bil-ly Boy, Bil-ly Boy? Can she
oft-en seen in church, Bil-ly Boy, Bil-ly Boy? Is she
How tall is she, Bil-ly Boy, Bil-ly Boy?
How old is she, Bil-ly Boy, Bil-ly Boy?

Where are you go-ing, charm-ing Bil-ly? I am going to see my wife; she's the
make a cher-ry pie, charm-ing Bil-ly? Yes, she can make a cher-ry pie quick as
oft-en seen in church, charm-ing Bil-ly? Yes, she's oft-en seen in church, with a
How tall is she, charm-ing Bil-ly? She is tall as an-y pine, and straight
How old is she, charm-ing Bil-ly? She's three times seven twen-ty-

joy of my life; But she's a young thing and can-not leave her moth-er. 2 Can she
you can wink an eye, But she's a young thing and can-not leave her moth-er. 3 Is she
bon-net white as perch, But she's a young thing and can-not leave her moth-er.
as a pump-kin vine, But she's a young thing and can-not leave her moth-er.
-eight and e-leven, But she's a young thing and can-not leave her moth-er.

BINGO

There was a farm-er had a dog; Bin-go was his name, sir; B-i-n-g-o go!
Right hand to your part-ner; Left hand to your neigh-bour, B-i-n-g-o go!

B-i-n-g-o go! B-i-n-g-o go! Bin-go was his name, sir.
B-i-n-g-o go! B-i-n-g-o go! Bin-go was his name, sir.

THE NEEDLE'S EYE

The nee-dle's eye, that doth sup-ply The thread that runs so

tru-ly; There's ma-ny a lass that I've let pass, Be-cause I want-ed

you-ly. With a bow so neat, And a kiss so sweet, We

do in-tend, be-fore we end, To have this cou-ple meet.

THREE DUKES WENT A-RIDING

Here comes two dukes a-rid-ing, a-rid-ing, a-rid-ing, Here
Oh, what you rid-ing here for, here for, here for? Oh,
We're rid-ing here to get mar-ried, mar-ried, mar-ried. We're
Won't you marry one of us, sir, — us, sir, — us, sir? Won't

come two dukes a-rid-ing; Tra-ran-si-tan-si-te!
what you rid-ing here for? Tra-ran-si-tan-si-te!
rid-ing here to get mar-ried, Tra-ran-si-tan-si-te!
you marry one of us, sir? Tra-ran-si-tan-si-te!

You're all too black and greasy, greasy, greasy,
You're all too black and greasy,
Tra-ransi-tansi-te!

[down the hall,
Then up the kitchen and down the hall, down the hall,
Then up the kitchen and down the hall,
Tra-ransi-tansi-te!

Choose the fairest one of all, one of all, one of all,
Choose the fairest one of all,
Tra-ransi-tansi-te!

AH, POOR BIRD

Ah, poor bird! Take thy flight,

back to beginning

Far a-bove the sor-rows of this sad world.

* 2nd, 3rd and 4th voices enter when the previous voice has reached here

I HAVE A LITTLE PONY

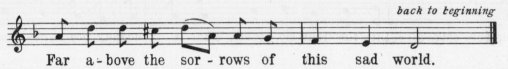

I have a lit-tle po - ny His name is Dap-ple Grey,— I___
I love my lit-tle po - ny He's safe-ly car-ried me,— And___

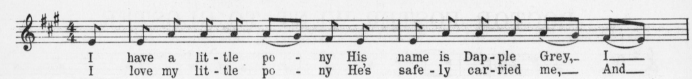

lent him to a la - dy To ride a mile a-way. She whipp'd him and she lash'd him She
corn, and hay, and sta - ble, Has on-ly asked for fee. I've sad-dled him and ridden him On

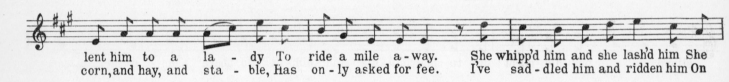

rode him thro' the mire— I___ would not lend my po-ny now For all the la-dy's hire.
man-y a sum-mer's day— And_ no one shall un-kind-ly use My lit-tle Dap-ple Grey.

FRERE JACQUES

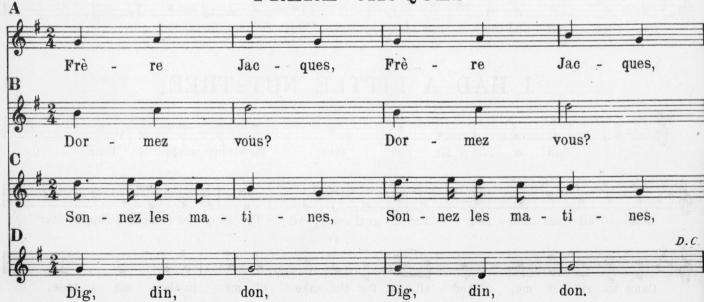

A

Frè - re Jac - ques, Frè - re Jac - ques,

B

Dor - mez vous? Dor - mez vous?

C

Son - nez les ma-ti - nes, Son - nez les ma-ti - nes,

D

D. C.

Dig, din, don, Dig, din, don.

*This Air is for four voices. When the first voice arrives at letter **B**, the second commences at **A**, the first continuing. When the second voice arrives at **B**, the third commences at **A**, and so on. When the first voice arrives at end of line **D**, the singer may re-start at **A**, forming an endless round.*

DING DONG BELL

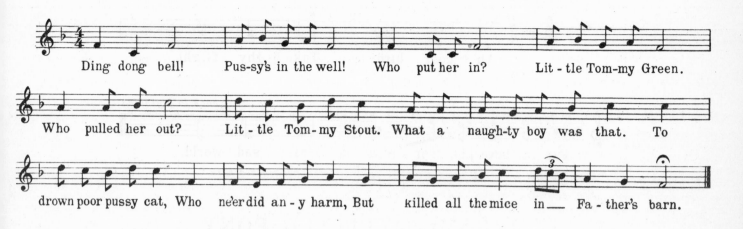

Ding dong bell! Pus-sy's in the well! Who put her in? Lit-tle Tom-my Green.

Who pulled her out? Lit-tle Tom-my Stout. What a naugh-ty boy was that. To

drown poor pussy cat, Who ne'er did an-y harm, But killed all the mice in__ Fa-ther's barn.

DOCTOR FOSTER WENT TO GLOSTER

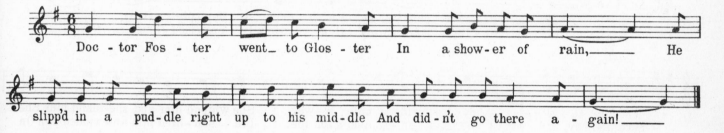

Doc-tor Fos-ter went__ to Glos-ter In a show-er of rain,____ He

slipp'd in a pud-dle right up to his mid-dle And did-n't go there a-gain!____

HEY DIDDLE DUMPLING

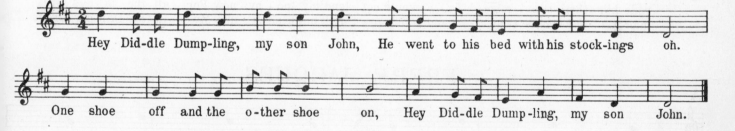

Hey Did-dle Dump-ling, my son John, He went to his bed with his stock-ings oh.

One shoe off and the o-ther shoe on, Hey Did-dle Dump-ling, my son John.

I HAD A LITTLE NUT-TREE

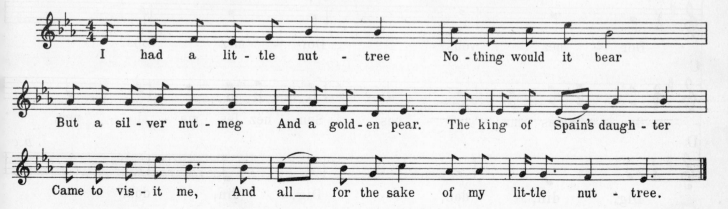

I had a lit-tle nut-tree No-thing would it bear

But a sil-ver nut-meg And a gold-en pear. The king of Spain's daugh-ter

Came to vis-it me, And all__ for the sake of my lit-tle nut-tree.

THE JOLLY MILLER

There was a jol-ly mil-ler and he lived by him-self, As the wheel went round he— made his pelf. One hand in the hop-per and the oth-er in the bag, As the wheel went round he— made his grab.

THE KING OF FRANCE

The king of France, the king of France, with twice ten thou-sand men, They all of them went up the hill, And then came back a - gain.

IL ÉTAIT UNE BERGÈRE

Il é - tait un' ber - gè - re, Et ron, ron, ron, pe - tit
El - le fit un fro - ma - ge, Et ron, ron, ron, pe - tit
Le chat, qui la re - gar - de, Et ron, ron, ron, pe - tit
"Si tu y mets la pat - te, Et ron, ron, ron, pe - tit

pa - ta - pon, Il é - tait un' ber - gè - re Qui
pa - ta - pon, El - le fit un fro - ma - ge, Du
pa - ta - pon, Le chat qui la re - gar - de, A
pa - ta - pon, Si tu y mets la pat - te, Tu

gar - dait ses mou - tons, ron, ron, Qui gar - dait ses mou - tons.—
lait de ses mou - tons, ron, ron, Du lait de ses mou - tons.—
un p'tit air fri - pon, ron, ron, A un p'tit air fri - pon.—
au - ras du bâ - ton, ron, ron, Tu au - ras du bâ - ton."—

Il n'y mit pas la patte,
Et ron, ron, ron, petit patapon,
Il n'y mit pas la patte,
Il y mit le menton,
   Ron, ron,
Il y mit le menton.

La Bergère en colère,
Et ron, ron, ron, petit patapon,
La Bergère en colère,
Battit son p'tit chaton,
   Ron, ron,
Battit son p'tit chaton.

THE LION AND THE UNICORN

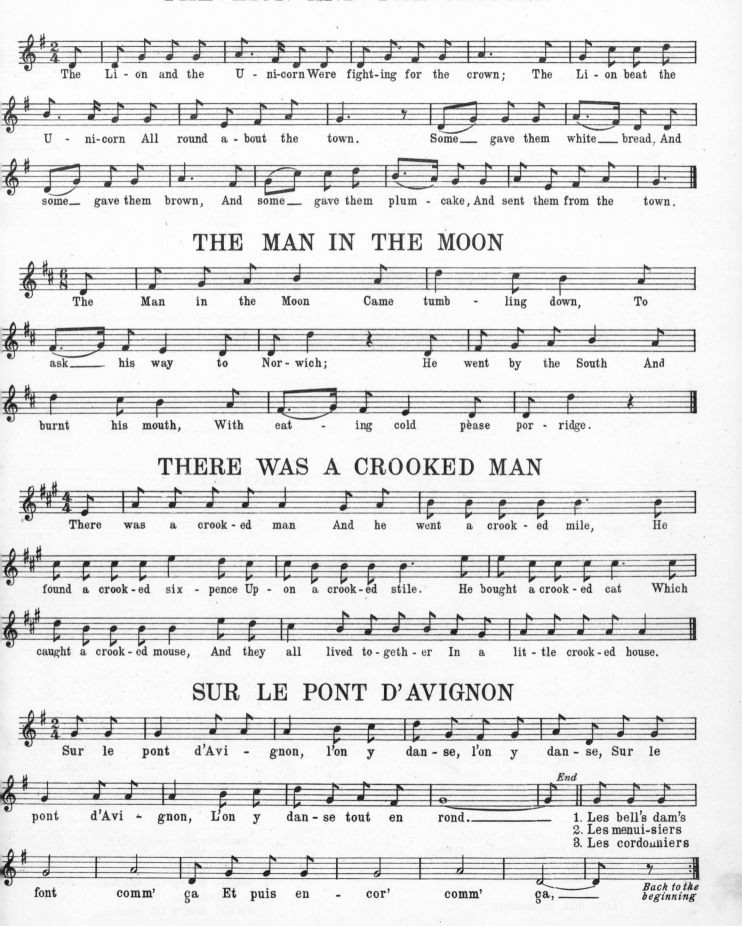

The Li-on and the U-ni-corn Were fight-ing for the crown; The Li-on beat the U-ni-corn All round a-bout the town. Some gave them white bread, And some gave them brown, And some gave them plum-cake, And sent them from the town.

THE MAN IN THE MOON

The Man in the Moon Came tumb-ling down, To ask his way to Nor-wich; He went by the South And burnt his mouth, With eat-ing cold pease por-ridge.

THERE WAS A CROOKED MAN

There was a crook-ed man And he went a crook-ed mile, He found a crook-ed six-pence Up-on a crook-ed stile. He bought a crook-ed cat Which caught a crook-ed mouse, And they all lived to-geth-er In a lit-tle crook-ed house.

SUR LE PONT D'AVIGNON

Sur le pont d'Avi-gnon, l'on y dan-se, l'on y dan-se, Sur le pont d'Avi-gnon, L'on y dan-se tout en rond.

End

1. Les bell's dam's
2. Les menui-siers
3. Les cordonniers

font comm' ça Et puis en-cor' comm' ça,

Back to the beginning

LAVENDER'S BLUE

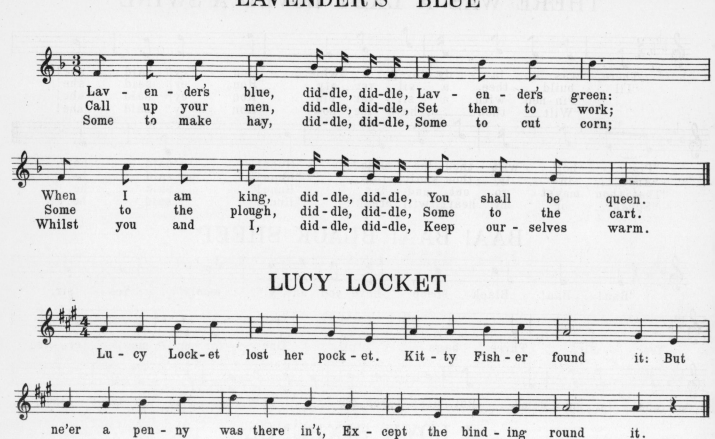

Lav - en - der's blue, did-dle, did-dle, Lav - en - der's green:
Call up your men, did-dle, did-dle, Set them to work;
Some to make hay, did-dle, did-dle, Some to cut corn;

When I am king, did-dle, did-dle, You shall be queen.
Some to the plough, did-dle, did-dle, Some to the cart.
Whilst you and I, did-dle, did-dle, Keep our-selves warm.

LUCY LOCKET

Lu - cy Lock-et lost her pock - et. Kit - ty Fish - er found it: But

ne'er a pen - ny was there in't, Ex - cept the bind - ing round it.

OH DEAR! WHAT CAN THE MATTER BE?

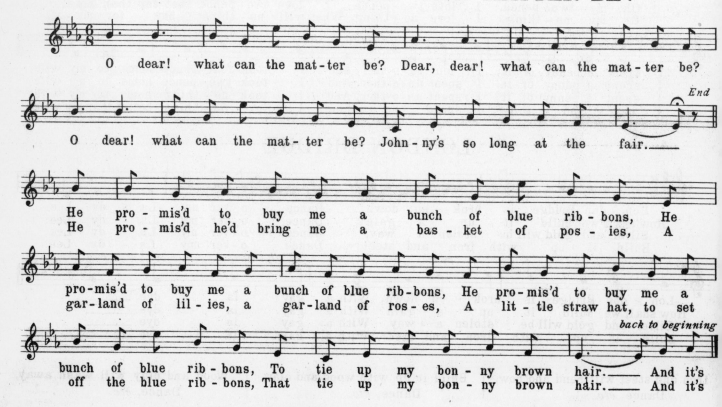

O dear! what can the mat-ter be? Dear, dear! what can the mat-ter be?

O dear! what can the mat-ter be? John-ny's so long at the fair.

He pro - mis'd to buy me a bunch of blue rib - bons, He
He pro - mis'd he'd bring me a bas - ket of pos - ies, A

pro-mis'd to buy me a bunch of blue rib-bons, He pro-mis'd to buy me a
gar-land of lil-ies, a gar-land of ros-es, A lit-tle straw hat, to set

bunch of blue rib-bons, To tie up my bon-ny brown hair.____ And it's
off the blue rib-bons, That tie up my bon-ny brown hair.____ And it's

THERE WAS A LADY LOVED A SWINE

There was a la-dy loved a swine, "Hon-ey," said she!
"I'll build_ thee a sil-ver sty, "Hon-ey," said she!
"Pin-ned with a sil-ver pin, "Hon-ey," said she!
"Wilt_ thou_ have me now, "Hon-ey," said she!

"Pig-hog, wilt thou be mine?" "Hunc!" said he.
"And_ in it thou shalt lie," "Hunc!" said he.
"That thou may'st go out and in," "Hunc!" said he.
"Speak,_ or my heart will break!" "Hunc!" said he.

BAA! BAA! BLACK SHEEP

"Baa! Baa! Black sheep have you an-y wool?" "Yes sir,

Yes . sir, Three bags full; One for my mas-ter, and

one for my dame, But none for the lit-tle boy That cries in the lane!"

I LOVE SIXPENCE

I love six-pence, I love six-pence, I love six-pence bet-ter than my life.
Oh, my four-pence, I love four-pence, I love four-pence bet-ter than my life.
Oh, my two-pence, I love two-pence, I love two-pence bet-ter than my life.
Oh, my no-thing, I love no-thing, What will no-thing buy for my wife?

I spent a penny of it, I lent an-o-ther, And I took four-pence home to my wife.
I spent a penny of it, I spent an-o-ther, And I took two-pence home to my wife.
I spent a penny of it, I spent an-o-ther, And I took no-thing home to my wife.
I have no-thing, I spend_ no-thing, I love no-thing better than my wife!

LONDON BRIDGE

Lon-don Bridge is brok-en down, Dance o-ver my La-dy Lee:
How shall we build it up a-gain? Dance o-ver my La-dy Lee:
Silver and gold will be stolen a-way, Dance o-ver my La-dy Lee:
Build it up with iron and steel, Dance o-ver my La-dy Lee:

Lon-don Bridge is brok-en down, With a gay la-dye._
How shall we build it up a-gain? With a gay la-dye._
Silver and gold will be stolen a-way, With a gay la-dye._
Build it up with iron and steel, With a gay la-dye._

Iron and steel will bend and bow, | Build it up with wood and clay, | Wood and clay will wash away,
Dance, etc. | Dance, etc. | Dance, etc.

THERE WAS A MAN OF THESSALY

There was a man of Thes-sa-ly And he was won-drous wise,___ He

jumped in-to a quick-set hedge And scratched out both his eyes. But

when he found his eyes were out, With all his might and main He

jumped in-to an-oth-er hedge, And scratched them in a-gain!

THREE WISE MEN OF GOTHAM

Thee wise men of Go-tham Went to sea in a bowl;

Had the bowl been strong-er My tale had been long-er.

WEE WILLIE WINKIE

Wee Wil-lie Win-kie, rins thro' the toun,

up-stairs and down-stairs in his night gown, Tir-ling at the win-dow,

cry-ing at the lock "Are the weans in their bed, For it's now ten o' clock?"

Lowe & Brydone Printers Ltd., London, N.W. 10.